THE MENTAL HEALTH ACT COMMISSION

FIFTH BIENNIAL REPORT 1991-1993

*Laid before Parliament by the
Secretary of State for Health
pursuant to Section 121 (10) of the
Mental Health Act 1983*

DECEMBER 1993

London: HMSO

CONTENTS

Page

Appendices

CHAIRMAN'S FOREWORD

While acting for the ten years of its existence as the public watchdog over the rights and interests of patients detained in hospitals and mental nursing homes, the Commission is now finding itself increasingly distracted, if not diverted from its main function of visiting, to its other statutory remit of keeping "under review the exercise of the powers and discharge of the duties conferred or imposed" by the Mental Health Act 1983. A reflection of the latter activity has been the recent attention paid to the effectiveness of the law to ensure that mentally disordered people can receive care and treatment in the community, a topic that was raised by the Royal College of Psychiatrists' proposal for a Community Supervision Order and the Department of Healths's urgent response in the form of a proposed new provision for a supervised discharge order.

The apparent need for an additional power over mentally disordered people is no more than an accurate barometer of the officially — instigated shift in emphasis, if not in practical reality of mental health services, from closed institutions to community care. The Commission, not unnaturally casts envious eyes to its two sister organisations — the Scottish Mental Welfare Commission and the Northern Ireland Mental Health Commission — which supervise the whole range of mental health services in their respective parts of the United Kingdom.

Much of the Commission's thinking and forward planning, therefore, has been directed not just to the needed improvement of its policy and practices relating to its visiting function but also to its future role and function in the changing climate of the mental health system. There have been a number of important developments in the last 2 years in the provision of mental health care generally; perhaps the most significant was the publication of the Health of the Nation White Paper which identified mental illness as one of the five key areas in its health strategy. The Commission will be playing its part in the implementation of that strategy.

The most immediate and pressing concern of the Commission, however, is the crisis in the inner cities. The rapid through-put and premature discharge of detained patients, combined with inadequate provisions for their aftercare, is so serious that the Commission is calling urgently for remedial action, starting with a review of the provision of in-patient beds in the large urban centres. The nature and size of the problem is briefly described in Chapter 3 of this Biennial Report.

The Commission has gone on record as advocating a thorough going review of the 1983 Act, much in the manner that the Percy Commission did in 1957 on mental illness and mental deficiency and which led to the Mental Health Act 1959 which established the modern legislative framework for the care and treatment of mentally disordered people. The 1983 Act was a major event, updating many of the principles and practices that underline the provision of care and treatment to detained patients. Now that the psychiatric profession, working increasingly in a multi-disciplinary setting, is being directed to patient care outside the institution, the need for a different legislative framework is indicated. The Commission's Memorandum, put to the Secretary of State at its tenth anniversary, is reproduced at Appendix 16. Part of the process for law reform is stimulated by the impressive review by the Law Commission of the intractable problem of decision-making by mentally incapacitated persons. The Commission itself, if it is to be allocated a watch dog role in the new mental health environment of community care and multiplying hospital units for both detained and de facto detained patients, will need a refurbished legislative framework which takes into account the new opportunities for monitoring services and quality assurance provided by the recent radical reforms in the provision of health and social care.

Quality assurance begins at home. The Commission has for some time been engaged in reviewing itself, and latterly in devising a more efficient, and expectantly effective, method of carrying out its present statutory functions and any additional functions that might be remitted. By the end of this year the Commission will be presenting proposals for re-structuring its membership and targeting more precisely its activities.

The experience of the decade of the Commission has pinpointed deficiencies in the role and function of the Commission. Only a fraction — sometimes less than 20% — of patients detained in hospital during a year have been seen by a member of the Commission. This is because a hospital is visited only annually by the Commission. Patients are admitted on average it is believed only for 21 days and most are in and out between visits from the Commission. The three Special Hospitals, with their lengthy (average 6 years) detention of patients, have necessarily attracted frequent visits from the Commission. Yet, despite heightened visiting activity, the Commission failed to uncover, or at least to alert the public to, substandard care and treatment of patients. The Ashworth Inquiry, in which four Commissioners, in their personal capacity, exposed a "stagnant, brutalising closed institution", stung the Commission into a most critical and creative self examination. It is in the spirit of such self-criticism and a desire to do better next time that the Commission looks forward to the next decade with a sense of dedication and cautious optimism that it will be a more effective protector of the rights and interests of people detained in hospitals and mental nursing homes.

1.
THE FUNCTIONS OF THE COMMISSION

The Mental Health Act Commission (MHAC) is a Special Health Authority, established in 1983. It comprises some ninety part-time members, including lay persons, lawyers, doctors, nurses, social workers, psychologists and other specialists (see Appendix 1 for list of members). It has a Chairman and Vice Chairman and is staffed by Civil Servants seconded from the Department of Health.

The functions of the MHAC are:

a. To keep under review the power and duties conferred on or imposed on it by the Mental Health Act 1983 (The Act) in respect of patients detained or liable to be detained under the Act.

b. To visit and interview, in private, patients detained under the Act in hospitals and mental nursing homes.

c. To investigate complaints in certain circumstances.

d. To review decisions to withhold the mail of patients detained in Special Hospitals.

e. To appoint:

   i. registered medical practitioners to give second opinions in cases where this is required by the Act; and

   ii. other persons to certify capacity to consent under Section 57 of the Act.

f. To monitor the Code of Practice and advise Ministers on amendments.

g. To publish a biennial report.

h. To offer advice to Ministers on matters falling within the Commission's remit.

Appendix 2 contains extracts from the Mental Health Act concerning the Commission and also the relevant statutory instruments.

Reports about the undertaking of these responsibilities will be found in later chapters.

2.
THE COMMISSION'S STRUCTURE, ADMINISTRATION AND PURSUIT OF QUALITY

2.1 Introduction

The Commission's administration has been centralised in Nottingham for three years. The Fourth Biennial Report (Chapter 2) outlined the new structure and reported on the objectives of centralisation. The time is now right to review how far the Commission has achieved those objectives which were:

a. To enable the Commission, within its budget, to carry out its statutory functions (Chapter 1) and the monitoring of the Code of Practice (Chapter 9) in
as effective and efficient a manner as possible, and also with as great a national consistency as possible.

b. To enable the Commission to make a more effective contribution at a general policy level on issues relevant to its statutory remit by, in part, making more use of the information acquired by members of the Commission carrying out its statutory functions.

In order to do this it is necessary to describe in a little detail the current structure of the Commission (para 2.2 below).

2.2 The Structure

(a) Commission Visiting Teams (CVTs)

Each Commissioner, with the exception of the Chairman, is a member of one of 7 CVTs. Each CVT is responsible for visiting all hospitals (other than the Special Hospitals) and Mental Nursing Homes; meeting with Social Services Departments; and investigating complaints in a particular geographical area. Each of the areas relate to those covered by two or three Regional Health Authorities (map on page 12). One CVT is responsible for the whole of Wales together with one English Regional Health Authority.

Each CVT has a staff support team (page 13) in the Nottingham office which also organises the Commission's response to requests for doctors under Part IV of the Mental Health Act. Each CVT has a Convenor appointed from among its membership, who takes overall responsibility including some elements of financial control, for the work of the team.

(b) Special Hospital Panels (SHPs)

With the exception of the Chairman and Vice Chairman each Commissioner is a member of one of the three Special Hospitals Panels relating to Broadmoor, Ashworth and Rampton. This is because approximately one fifth of patients detained under the Mental Health Act are in the Special Hospitals and the Commission has decided to continue to visit the Special Hospitals with much more frequency than other hospitals.

The Special Hospital Panels also have their own Convenor and Complaints Convenor, and administrative support staff. The support staff also administer a CVT, in addition to their SHP work (page 13).

(c)   National Standing Committees (NSCs)

The Commission has 10 National Standing Committees and most Commissioners are members of at least one Committee. Four NSCs (Visiting, Consent to Treatment, Complaints, and Research and Information) oversee the four fundamental operational responsibilities of the Commission. The remaining NSCs take responsibility for discrete policy areas. A list of NSCs and their respective terms of reference can be found at Appendix 3. Because of financial constraints some of the National Standing Committees were not operational for part of the Report period.

(d)   Central Policy Committee (CPC)

Membership of CPC, which is governed by the Statutory Instrument 894 (SI 1983/894) at Appendix 2 comprises the Commission Chairman and Vice Chairman, plus ten other Commission members appointed by the Secretary of State. It has overall responsibility for the activities of the Commission and in particular for overseeing financial control of the organisation. CPC has a number of specifically designated functions (see SI 1983/894). The full Committee meets approximately every two months. There is also a Finance Sub Committee which meets on a regular basis, to review and control the Commission's expenditure.

(e)   Ethnic issues within the Commission

The Policy on Race developed for the Commission (and published in the Fourth Biennial Report) has been actively monitored by the National Standing Committee (NSC) on Race and Culture in co-operation with the Chief Executive. The Commission is pleased that its Central Policy Committee (CPC) now includes black members and expects that the Minister will ensure that both the Commission's membership and its CPC will continue to have an appropriate ethnic mix in future years. The NSC on Race and Culture is now drafting a policy on race in relation to the more general activities of the Commission.

The Commission held training days on race and culture for Commission members in June and October 1992 and similar days are planned during the next year. Race and Culture was selected as the main theme to be addressed at the Commission Conference in October 1993.

2.3   Meeting the Objectives of the Commission

It is now true to say that centralisation of the administration has enabled the Commission to achieve the objectives outlined at 2.1 above.

In a relatively short space of time the Commission has succeeded in improving its level of performance both in terms of consistency and in its ability to respond quickly and effectively to policy issues. In the long term this should result in the Commission being a much more positive influence in the mental health field than was possible in the period prior to centralisation.

Part IV of this report demonstrates that the Commission is not standing still and is continuing to assess how it can improve its structure further (Chapter 16). At the same time it is responding to the changes in the NHS which are having a considerable impact on the Commission's statutory visiting function. The development of Trusts, and the increasing number of small units containing detained patients has meant that updating records and deploying Commissioners effectively has become more challenging (Chapter 3). The 1983 Mental Health Act was drafted at a time when the majority of detained patients were nearly all housed in large institutions. Now this is no longer the case, the Commission recognises both the need to adapt its own organisation and to consider how the legislation needs to be changed to make it more relevant to the current situation (Chapter 17).

The Commission, as an organisation composed of approximately 90 part-time members has always been faced with an immense administrative task in trying to co-ordinate its activities in the most effective way.

The following steps have been taken over the previous two years to develop a more consistent approach throughout the Commission and to promote and develop high standards of performance:

(a)   Standardisation of policies and procedures

Although a considerable amount of work had been done in the first year after centralisation to standardise policies and procedures, the last two years have seen the completion and further refinement of the Commission's Visiting Policy and Procedure, Complaints Policy and Procedure and, Special Hospital Visiting Procedure (Appendices 8 and 9).

Further details will be found in the relevant chapters of the report.

In general terms the Commission is constantly reviewing its procedures in accordance with the changes in the NHS and its own operational needs. Particular emphasis has been placed on establishing more effective monitoring procedures, (particularly in relation to complaints investigations and second opinion doctor reports), and the development of performance indicators (Chapters 3, 6 and 7).

(b)   Development of performance indicators, and provision of information

Over the next two years the Commission intends, in conjunction with the Audit Commission, to further develop performance indicators in relation to its visiting activities. This will involve setting quantitative and qualitative standards for Commissioners and Commission staff. This will greatly assist the Commission in targeting its resources much more effectively. Preliminary work on this has already begun (Chapters 3 and 19).

In time, the Commission intends to publicise widely its standards in accordance with the Patients Charter.

Other activities which are in hand to increase the amount of information which the Commission makes available to those concerned are:-

   i. a leaflet explaining how the Commission investigates complaints;

   ii. a leaflet explaining the second opinion procedure.

The Commission has revised and issued a new general information leaflet on the work of the Commission. This is currently with the Welsh Office for translation into Welsh.

In the previous Biennial Report, it was announced that the Department of Health had agreed that the Commission could from time to time publish Practice Notes giving advice on issues about which it receives numerous requests and which are not dealt with in the Code of Practice.

The first of these, which deals with the issues surrounding the administration of clozapine, has now been issued. Two others, one about the transfer of patients between hospitals on Section 5(2), and another on the administration of medicine by nurses, will be published shortly. The Commission has continued to receive numerous requests for advice on an enormous range of issues, particularly from mental health professionals and administrators. For the reasons outlined in the Fourth Biennial Report, the Commission is limited in its ability to help in this matter, primarily because it has no remit to provide formal legal advice.

The Commission's position was clearly laid out in a letter which was issued to all Health Authorities, Social Services Departments and Trusts on 29th January 1992. A copy of the letter is reproduced at Appendix 5. The regular issue of Practice Notes which will be available to those involved in the provision of mental health services as well as to Commissioners and Commission staff is a response to this dilemma. Together with use of the Code of Practice, these Notes should contribute to the achievement of consistency and effectiveness in the provision of patient care.

(c) Computerisation

The first stage of the Commission's computer project — that is, the computerisation of administrative procedures in relation to visiting has now been completed, and a finance package has also been implemented. Financial constraints have meant that there have been some delays in the implementation of the next phases of the project. Once further resources have been made available by the Department of Health, it is intended to proceed with the computerisation of Consent to Treatment information. Some progress on this has already been achieved 'in house' (Chapter 7).

The computer has been one of the main tools which has enabled the Commission to achieve consistency in its procedures, and more effectively collate the mass of information it collects. Thanks are due to the Commission staff who have shown considerable enthusiasm for the project as well as being very patient whilst initial problems with the system have been overcome. Thanks are also due to the Information Systems

Directorate division of the Department of Health for their advice and support.

(d) Finance

The Mental Health Act Commission, as a Special Health Authority, is financed directly by the Department of Health with a contribution from the Welsh Office. The Commission's expenditure, which is cash limited in the same way as other health authorities, is summarised at Appendix 4.

Throughout the previous two years the Commission has reviewed, and tightened control of its finances. Computerisation, the devolution of some aspects of financial control to CVT and SHP Convenors, and the development of the Finance Sub-Committee have all assisted in this process.

The Commission is due from April 1994 to become an 'independent budget' holder. In practical terms this means that although, the Commission will continue to receive funding direct from the Department of Health, it will have more freedom in deciding how and where its money will be spent.

DISTRIBUTION OF COMMISSION VISITING TEAMS

CVT Regional Health Authority Area/Wales

1. East Anglia/NE Thames
2. North West Thames/Oxford
3. South East Thames/South West Thames
4. Wessex/South Western
5. Trent/Yorkshire and Northern
6. Wales/West Midlands
7. Mersey/North Western

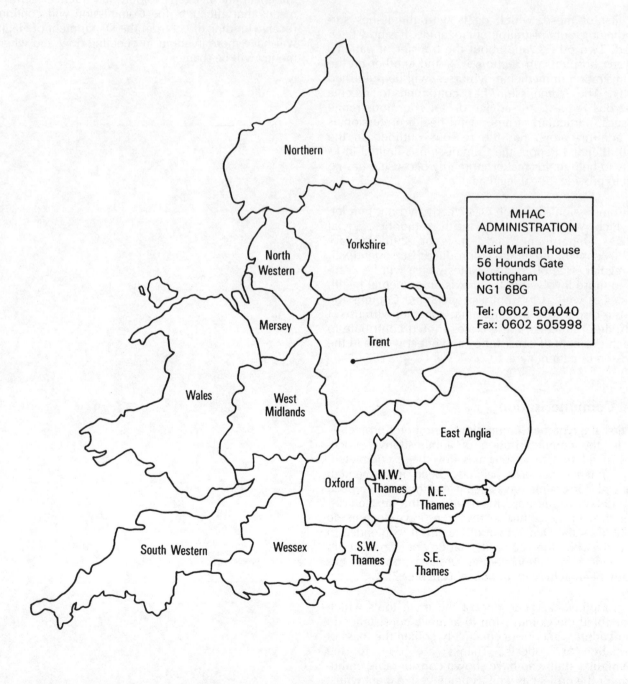

MHAC
ADMINISTRATION

Maid Marian House
56 Hounds Gate
Nottingham
NG1 6BG

Tel: 0602 504040
Fax: 0602 505998

ADMINISTRATION GROUP STAFFING AT

30th JUNE 1993

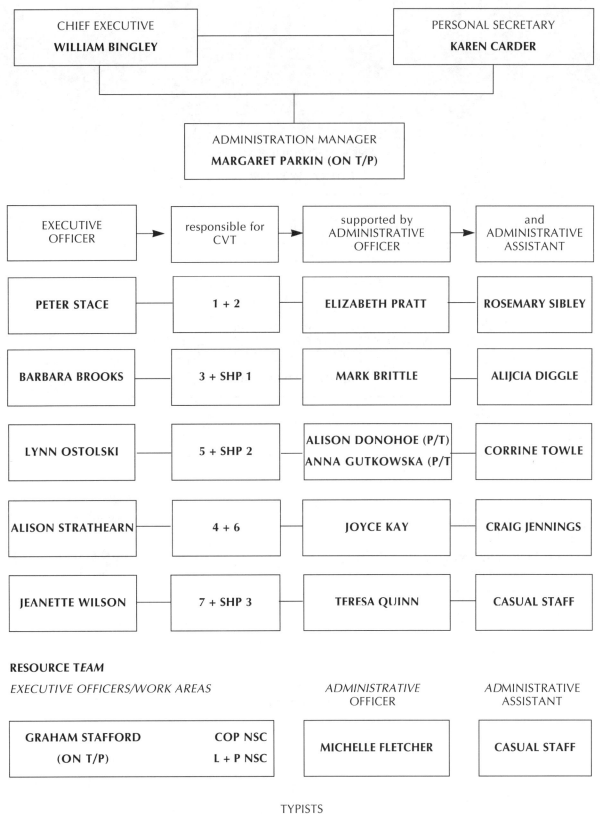

| CHIEF EXECUTIVE
WILLIAM BINGLEY | PERSONAL SECRETARY
KAREN CARDER |

ADMINISTRATION MANAGER
MARGARET PARKIN (ON T/P)

EXECUTIVE OFFICER	responsible for CVT	supported by ADMINISTRATIVE OFFICER	and ADMINISTRATIVE ASSISTANT
PETER STACE	1 + 2	**ELIZABETH PRATT**	**ROSEMARY SIBLEY**
BARBARA BROOKS	3 + SHP 1	**MARK BRITTLE**	**ALIJCIA DIGGLE**
LYNN OSTOLSKI	5 + SHP 2	**ALISON DONOHOE (P/T)** **ANNA GUTKOWSKA (P/T**	**CORRINE TOWLE**
ALISON STRATHEARN	4 + 6	**JOYCE KAY**	**CRAIG JENNINGS**
JEANETTE WILSON	7 + SHP 3	**TERESA QUINN**	**CASUAL STAFF**

RESOURCE TEAM

EXECUTIVE OFFICERS/WORK AREAS · *ADMINISTRATIVE OFFICER* · *ADMINISTRATIVE ASSISTANT*

GRAHAM STAFFORD	COP NSC	**MICHELLE FLETCHER**	**CASUAL STAFF**
(ON T/P)	L + P NSC		

TYPISTS

| **MECHELE PAYNE**
KAREN DICKMAN
TRACY CLARKE |

POLICY AND FINANCE GROUP STAFFING AT 30th JUNE 1993

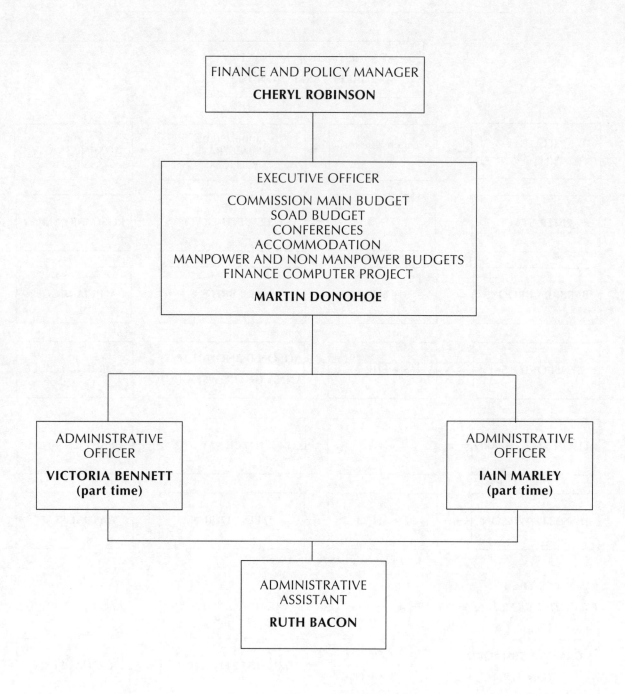

FINANCE AND POLICY MANAGER

CHERYL ROBINSON

EXECUTIVE OFFICER

COMMISSION MAIN BUDGET
SOAD BUDGET
CONFERENCES
ACCOMMODATION
MANPOWER AND NON MANPOWER BUDGETS
FINANCE COMPUTER PROJECT

MARTIN DONOHOE

ADMINISTRATIVE
OFFICER

**VICTORIA BENNETT
(part time)**

ADMINISTRATIVE
OFFICER

**IAIN MARLEY
(part time)**

ADMINISTRATIVE
ASSISTANT

RUTH BACON

PROJECTS TEAM STAFFING AT
30th JUNE 1993

PROJECTS MANAGER	EXECUTIVE OFFICER
ALISON COONEY **HEO.**	COMPLAINTS NSC VISITING NCS CONSENT NSC COMPUTER MANAGEMENT R & I NSC **ANDREW KAY**

KEY INDEX

CVT	COMMISSION VISITING TEAM
NSC	NATIONAL STANDING COMMITTEE
	R & I – RESEARCH AND INFORMATION
	COP – CODE OF PRACTICE
	L & P – LEGAL AND PARLIAMENTARY
SHPA	ASHWORTH SPECIAL HOSPITAL
SHPB	BROADMOOR SPECIAL HOSPITAL
SHPR	RAMPTON SPECIAL HOSPITAL
T/P	TEMPORARY PROMOTION
P/T	PART TIME

3.
VISITS TO HOSPITALS (OTHER THAN SPECIAL HOSPITALS) AND MENTAL NURSING HOMES AND MEETINGS WITH SOCIAL SERVICES DEPARTMENTS

3.1 Visits to Hospitals and Mental Nursing Homes

The Commission visits patients detained under the Mental Health Act in hospitals, Special Hospitals (Chapter 5) registered mental nursing homes, (all private hospitals are at law mental nursing homes) and units spanning the whole range of provisions for inpatient care. The previous Biennial Reports have described in considerable detail the purpose of visits and how they have been organised.

On average each hospital or registered mental nursing home is visited by members of the Commission once a year. Units which provide high security care for patients detained under the Mental Health Act, such as Regional Secure Units, and some secure mental nursing homes in the private sector, are visited more frequently.

In such establishments patient freedoms are self evidently more restricted and the more frequent visits enable members of the Commission to keep under review the care of those patients who during their detention require various degrees of security. Details of the numbers of visits undertaken during the period under review are given at Appendix 6.

3.2 Meetings with Social Services Departments

Members of the Commission have continued to meet with all Social Services Departments at least once every two years to discuss the operation of statutory assessment and admission procedures for people requiring detention under the Mental Health Act and the effectiveness of their compliance with the provisions of Section 117 of the Act. Members of the Commission continue to monitor the use made of guardianship, the training of Approved Social Workers and the implementation of guidance contained in the Code of Practice which is relevant to Social Services Departments and Approved Social Workers. Some issues arising from such meetings are referred to in Chapter 14.

3.3 Joint Visits by Commissioners to Services provided by Trusts, Health Authorities and Social Services Departments

The trend reported in the two previous Biennial Reports towards joint visits by Commissioners to services provided by Trusts, Health Authorities and Social Services Departments has continued. In some areas such joint visits are now the normal pattern. The Commission is thus able to comment effectively on the full service offered to detained patients. Joint visits are not so effective where geographical areas are not co-terminous; for example where Health Authorities relate to a number of Social Services Departments and vice-versa.

3.4 How the Commission Visits

Over the past two years the Commission has reviewed and gradually refined its visiting policies and procedures. The administrative procedures for arranging visits have been computerised. This should help achieve an improved standard in the planning and organisation of visits and meetings. It will also make a major contribution to the systematic collation of information gathered on visits and will enable the Commission to speak with greater authority about the issues that arise during the undertaking of this particular Commission statutory responsibility. The full implementation of the computer programme was not achieved until the end of this Biennial Report period, so the full benefits have not yet become apparent.

Concern was expressed in the Fourth Biennial Report that although Commissioners visit most hospitals and mental nursing homes once a year, most patients are detained for an average of 21 days which means that many detained patients are not seen by Commissioners. The Commission is currently undertaking a review of its role and function which will take account of this problem. (Chapter 16).

The changes in the way mental health care is now delivered, and in particular the run down of large psychiatric hospitals and their replacement with smaller units, is resulting in a rapid increase in the number of hospitals and mental nursing homes capable of receiving detained patients. The number of units on the Commission visiting programme has thus increased from 557 for the period 1987–1989 to 673 in the period 1991–1993.

The Commission has been aware of the need to keep under review the impact of the NHS and Community Care Act. The Commission has suggested standard clauses about the care of patients detained under the Act for inclusion in contracts between purchasers and providers. These have been included in the Health of the Nation Key Area Handbook — Mental Illness. They are also reproduced at Appendix 7 of this Report.

As predicted in the Fourth Biennial Report, the standardisation of Commission visiting procedures has resulted in greater attention being paid to measuring the impact of its visits and a higher degree of focus on issues to be reviewed by Commissioners on their visits. This is particularly true in relation to issues which the Commission has decided to examine on every visit — the impact of the Code of Practice and Section 58 procedures for example.

Over the next two years it is the Commission's objective to further develop performance indicators for visiting in conjunction with the Audit Commission. This will assist the Commission in monitoring more effectively both its own performance and that of the institutions which it visits (Chapter 19), and will enable the Commission to be more pro-active in pursuing issues with purchasers of mental health services.

3.5 Some Issues Affecting Patients in Hospitals and Mental Nursing Homes

In its visits to 673 units each year, the Commission has encountered a wide range of issues, some of which are referred to below.

(a) Crisis in inner-city mental health services

The Commission's concerns have been focused on the high through-put and rapid discharge of detained patients in inner city acute psychiatric beds (40% or more of admissions across inner London are admitted compulsorily under sections of the Mental Health Act). On some wards this proportion is 80–90%. The problem of high bed occupancy (sometimes as much as 120%) in large urban areas such as London, Manchester, Birmingham and Liverpool has become an increasing concern of Commissioners. The result of this overloading is that the patients may be prematurely discharged from hospital on leave, often at a few hours notice and not infrequently to unsupervised accommodation, to make way for more acutely disturbed patients to be admitted. Alternatively patients may be admitted to a Unit many miles away. For example patients from Manchester are admitted to Units in Cheshire and Lancashire.

Implementation of Section 117 Aftercare and the Care Programme Approach is barely evident in many inner city acute units. The high morbidity levels in the inner city populations, lack of alternatives to admission, problems of homelessness, and poor community service, are contributing factors to the crisis in inner-city mental health services.

The Commission now regards the situation as serious and recognises an urgent need for remedial action which should include consideration of the following matters:

a. A review of the provision of in-patient beds.

b. A review of the siting and appropriateness of beds, safe houses, crisis centres and rehabilitation facilities.

c. A shift towards community based and comprehensive crisis and continuing care services available 24 hours a day.

d. A review of staff skills and their distribution.

e. A review of the balance of mental health care and social care funding on the part of purchasers.

f. The provision of increasing incentives for joint planning.

g. The setting of relevant targets and performance indicators; and

h. A review of the weighted capitation formula to ensure that levels of social morbidity are taken into account by Regional Health Authorities when making allocations to District Health Authorities.

The Commission will continue to keep this issue under urgent review.

(b) Ward environments

Whilst there has been effort on behalf of many hospitals to maintain the physical environment of psychiatric facilities, there are some where the physical surroundings and comforts available to patients are very poor. Members of the Commission continue to encounter unacceptable physical environments in a considerable number of hospitals. Commissioners have had occasion to comment generally on patients being given beds in dormitories or seclusion rooms with insufficient personal space, and have also found additional beds in corridors or day rooms.

Situations have also arisen where patients are moved at night to another ward in the hospital, or indeed to another site, to make way for a new admission; even when the patient has been given night medication.

Also of particular concern has been the physical environment in a number of the newer District General Hospitals, especially those using up-graded older buildings where there appears to be a lack of funds to maintain the decor and furnishing, and in some cases the absence of any planned maintenance programme.

(c) Patient mix

In many areas the patient mix, in terms of age and degree of disturbance, particularly on acute admission wards, has been of concern to Commissioners. In many instances less disturbed patients are placed with acutely psychotic patients. This is counter productive of therapeutic care and on a number of occasions patients have expressed fears for their own safety.

For example, a woman patient suffering puerperal depression and admitted informally together with her baby to a psychiatric unit said she was nervous of venturing away from her room and feared leaving her sleeping baby. She spent long periods standing as a sentry at her door. There were very obviously disturbed patients on the ward with no additional staff.

Commissioners have also noted that there are often one or two long-stay patients remaining on Admission Wards. Because of the pressure on the available beds these patients are frequently moved around the Ward or Unit from bed to bed as the clinical priorities of other patients require. As a consequence these longer stay patients are unable to personalise their bed space and appear to be in a continuous state of change and insecurity. It seems inappropriate that such patients should be cared for in acute accommodation once their assessment has been completed and a treatment plan drawn up.

(d) Staffing levels

Visiting Commissioners have frequently noted the inadequate number of nursing staff available on acute admission wards. Given that the percentage of disturbed patients admitted to these wards is growing, it is strikingly evident that the remaining patients, many of whom are informal, frequently receive minimal therapeutic input. Very often at one time there may be two or three acutely psychotic patients in the Unit who fully occupy the staff. For the majority of patients these Units appear to offer little beyond residential accommodation, the administration of medication and visits from junior doctors who do not have sufficient expertise. Patients often complain of "boredom" and Commissioners have found patients still lying in bed at 11.00 am, with little alternative activity available. There is a continuing shortage of occupational therapists and psychologists, which results in a lack of alternative treatment and patient activities.

When recently visiting a not untypical unit, Commissioners noted three disturbed patients in the Acute Admissions Ward. They were fully occupying the attention of five nurses, leaving just one nurse available to the remaining sixteen patients. The Commissioners over the past 3 years had raised the matter of patient mix with the hospital to little effect. Bed occupancy of the Unit is very high and at the time of the most recent visit 9 of the 21 beds were occupied by detained patients of whom 4 required individual nursing. Staffing comprised six persons, only 2 of whom were appropriately qualified. Two emergencies arose during the period of the Commissioners' visit which were dealt with by qualified staff leaving the unqualified nursing staff to provide routine treatment and care of the great majority of patients. This example which is not an isolated one illustrates a need to provide appropriate facilites and staff to deal with acutely disturbed patients. Such situations are unacceptable to the Commission.

It is worth noting that the nursing establishment on intensive care acute medical wards of General Hospitals is often at least double that of comparable psychiatric units with similar bed numbers. Consequently, qualified psychiatric nurses are often engaged in controlling, rather than treating, acutely disturbed behaviour. Commissioners believe that treatment may be determined by the availability of trained staff rather than the needs of patients.

Visiting Commissioners have noted that on many units the more senior trained psychiatric nursing staff spend much of their time occupied in administrative and clerical duties. It is felt that the appointment of Ward Clerks on acute units would liberate experienced nurses to engage in therapeutic activities with their patients and would facilitate improved record keeping.

(e)   Use of Section 5(2)

In the Fourth Biennial Report the Commission expressed the view that the clear guidance in the Code of Practice had undoubtedly contributed to an improvement in practice by Health Authorities and Trusts. The Commission has continued to keep the situation under review and has noted that in some units the holding power under Section 5(2) appears to be used more frequently than is desirable and that on some occasions its use has been authorised retrospectively. Section 5(2) can only be initiated by the patient's doctor if he is of the opinion that an application for the detention of the patient under the Act ought to be made in the prevailing circumstances. If the need to detain a patient is anticipated, a full assessment under Section 2 or 3 should take place.

Commissioners have found instances where S5(2) appears either to be used simply as a three day holding power, or lasts three days by default because the RMO has not informed the records officer as soon as a decision is taken not to proceed with assessment for compulsory detention or because the assessment process is not begun as soon as the Section 5(2) is implemented. In this context the Commission strongly recommends that a record be kept of the date and time of both beginning and end of the holding power under Section 5(2).

It has been noted that when audit has been undertaken the use of section 5(2) has declined.

The Commission and the Royal College of Psychiatrists both recognised the value of auditing Section 5(2) and other similar statutory procedures.

(f)   Issues in relation to the police

Over the two year period of the report Commissioners visiting Psychiatric Units have come across situations where police involvement in clinical situations has been a source of concern. Whilst good liaison with the police is essential it is important that this should not extend to their routine involvement in the treatment and care of patients and in particular they should not be routinely used for restraining a patient so that an injection can be administered. For example, Commissioners were recently informed of an incident where 13 police officers, 4 of whom were in riot gear, were called to assist in the administration of an injection to a detained patient. Similarly, in a newly opened psychiatric unit the police were summoned to assist nursing staff in giving a disturbed informal patient a neuroleptic injection. The police should not be used as members of nursing staff and every clinical situation, however challenging, should be handled by trained hospital staff, the units concerned being staffed accordingly.

There are also circumstances where the Approved Social Worker (ASW) has been in difficulty because of the violent nature of the patient and has asked for police assistance, without being able to specify the level of support required. In consequence, a number of police in riot gear have arrived, which has the effect of worsening rather than helping the situation.

(g)   Availability of interpreters

There has been a steady improvement in the availability of interpreters for patients whose first language is not English, but it is relatively rare that interpreters are trained for work in the mental health field. A problem remains in the case of some patients whose first language is relatively uncommon, such as Somali and Kurdish. There is a need for service providers to keep abreast of demographic trends. There is still, in some cases, a shortage of interpreters for patients with hearing impairments.

(h)   Racial issues

(i)   Ethnic monitoring
Some Purchasers in areas with relatively high numbers of minority ethnic communities have made it obligatory on Provider units to undertake ethnic monitoring but visiting teams are still unable very often to obtain a reliable ethnic breakdown of detained patients. (Chapter 13)

(ii)   Staff-patient interaction
Patients from minority ethnic communities frequently comment on the lack of 'talking treatments' being available, especially if their first language is not English. Furthermore, visiting Commissioners have noticed that rapport between psychiatric staff on the one hand and patients and/or their relatives on the other is often poor in the case of patients from such communities, leading to a feeling (on the part of the latter) that they are being discriminated against and misdiagnosed. It is extremely important for staff to counteract such feelings by exam-

ining staff-patient interactions and explaining to patients and their relatives the basis for diagnoses and treatment. (Chapter 13)

(iii)   Sensitivity of staff to racial and cultural issues

Although many provider units are attempting to improve their 'cultural sensitivity', the perception of service users and relations from minority ethnic communities is that it is rare for staff to show real understanding of institutional racism that affects black people and the cultural differences in illness presentation. The need for regular training of staff on race and culture is as evident now as it was in 1989 when the Commission's Third Biennial Report noted the need for better professional training in these fields. (Chapter 13)

(iv)   Mixed gender wards

Most in-patient units, except in the Secure Hospitals, provide mixed wards as a matter of policy. However, latterly, women patients, especially those from Asian communities, have begun to insist that they would prefer single gender wards or at least space within wards reserved for women patients. Some women feel very frightened to sleep in dormitories or single rooms leading from corridors that are easily accessible to male patients. Visiting teams have encountered several cases of attempted molestation in such settings. The Commission has encouraged units to provide locks on doors of single rooms in mixed wards and separate toilet facilities. However, the Commission believes that the whole policy regarding mixed wards may have to be reviewed in due course.

(i)   Mental nursing homes

Further issues relating to mental nursing homes are to be found at Chapter 14.

(j)   Older people with organic brain syndrome

The Commission is frequently asked to comment on whether or not older patients with dementia or other organic brain syndromes which impair their mental capacity to make reasoned judgements, should be detained for care and treatment under the provisions of the Act or can be admitted and cared for informally. There is, however, no hard and fast rule; the circumstances of every patient must be considered individually. The majority of older people with dementia who are mentally incapacitated are willing to accept the care and treatment offered to them. If admission is felt to be necessary, they can, at present, be admitted as informal patients, if that is felt to be in their best interests under the authority of common law.

The problem arises where the patient is actively refusing care and treatment and may persistently reject help from professional carers or actively seeks to leave the unit. In these cases, where the clinical team judges that the health or safety of the patient is at risk by allowing the patient freedom to remain outside the hospital or nursing home, then the team should seek an assessment for admission under the Act. Two common situations which cause difficulties are those where patients persistently wander away from the ward or unit and have to be returned against their wishes and where patients actively resist physical nursing care or medication but where staff have a duty to provide such interventions in order to preserve the health or safety of their patients.

There are a number of patients currently cared for in hospital who are detained "de facto" where it may be more appropriate for them to be formally detained under the Act. This would provide a surer legal framework for staff decision making and an opportunity for the care of the patients to be regularly reviewed by hospital managers and the Mental Health Review Tribunal.

Chapter 15 of the revised Code of Practice (1993) gives guidance on the treatment of those without capacity to consent. Chapter 18 of the Code considers in greater detail the issues of restraint and locked doors. It is recommended that clinical teams should review the status of patients with dementia, especially those in continuing care facilities to ensure that older patients legal rights are adequately safeguarded.

4.
THE COMMISSION IN WALES

4.1 Introduction

The jurisdiction of the 1983 Mental Health Act, and therefore the Commission's field of activity, covers Wales and England, and this Biennial Report in its entirety is relevant to both countries. However, there are important differences between the two countries, not only in language and culture, but in the way mental health services are administered. Central Government in Wales is administered by the Secretary of State for Wales through the Welsh Office in Cardiff, and it is this office which funds mental health services through District Health Authorities and local government. There are no Regional Health Authorities in Wales. In 1989 the Welsh Office published clear principles for service planning entitled "Mental Illness Services — A Strategy for Wales", and also issued a Mental Health Protocol setting specific targets. Other important publications by the Welsh Office are "The All Wales Mental Handicap Strategy" (1985), which is unique and has been much admired (it is reviewed yearly), and the "Report of the All Wales Advisory Group on Forensic Psychiatry" (1992). The Care Planning Approach applicable in England to some people with mental illnesses, does not apply to Wales, which follows principles laid down in the Mental Illness Strategy. The Secretary of State for Wales appoints 10 Commissioners, 7 of whom work in the Commission visiting team for Wales and the West Midlands. The Commission's 1990 conference was held in Cardiff.

4.2 The Commission and the Welsh Language

Of the three and three quarter million people who live in Wales, the preferred language of half a million, although bilingual in Welsh and English, is Welsh. The importance of the language is recognised in the 1993 Welsh Language Act. The Commission strongly supports the provision of leaflets in the Welsh language explaining patients' rights under the Mental Health Act, and the preparation of the Mental Health Act Code of Practice in Welsh. In its correspondence concerning Welsh affairs the Commission uses bilingually headed stationery, and is always ready to correspond in Welsh when requested. Four of the Commissioners visiting in Wales speak Welsh.

4.3 The Slow Revolution in Mental Health Services in Wales

Over many years now there has been a gradual change in the pattern of mental health services in Wales. An increasing emphasis has been placed on the provision of services close to people's homes, or even at their homes, so that there is less need for hospital services, which can be confined to acute cases and for special groups whose treatment and care cannot be provided elsewhere. Although similar changes have taken place in England, these developments have been promoted and steered in Wales by the Welsh Office Mental Illness Strategy and Protocol. One of the most striking consequences is the intention to close two large psychiatric hospitals, the North Wales Hospital in Clwyd and Parc Hospital in Mid Glamorgan, within the next 2 years.

Commissioners have been able to observe some of the consequences of this revolution from their experience of visiting mental illness services in Wales and the West Midlands over the last 2 years. There is no doubt that the changes on the whole are acceptable to patients, relatives, and service staff. They offer easily accessible services and a reduction in the need for hospital treatment. Commissioners have seen a number of excellent services in the community and in hospitals. Despite this, they would like to draw attention to some matters which are a cause of concern. In some areas there appear to be insufficient services for those most disabled by mental illness. There is also unacceptable pressure on some acute services.

4.4 A Shortage of Facilities for People with Long-Term Mental Illness

In some areas there appears to be a great need for day and residential services for people with long-term or cyclical mental illnesses. For a comparatively small number (those with severe disabilities) there is a need for high quality care by experienced staff in units or homes designed for this purpose. It is this kind of care which is currently provided, for example, by traditional mental hospitals such as the North Wales Hospital and Parc Hospital (and alternative arrangements will have to be made before these hospitals can close).

In some areas excellent provision is made in homes or units in the community. Where there is insufficient provision, however, serious problems can arise. Commissioners come across members of this group on some acute wards for the mentally ill. They have been admitted usually after committing some minor offence, after behaving oddly in public, or simply because they have grossly neglected their physical health. Some are admitted to hospital under statutory compulsion. With treatment and care their condition improves, but if alternative care is not available, staff are often reluctant to discharge them, and some may remain on acute wards for over a year in what is a very unsuitable environment. In addition, their presence reduces the number of beds available for acute cases, which can pose serious problems in those units (usually in District General Hospitals) which have a chronic shortage. Outside hospital their welfare is a cause of great anxiety to community mental health teams. The Commission feels strongly that special attention needs to be given to the provision of adequate services for this group.

4.5 Pressure on Acute Psychiatric Wards

It is the Commission's view that health authorities, in estimating bed numbers and staffing levels on acute psychiatric units, need to pay special attention to the prevailing local requirements. Some of these units work under great pressure due to shortage of beds, staff or community facilities, and this creates a disturbed, non-therapeutic, and even, at times, unsafe environment. While improved community services may eventually reduce admission rates, the loss of some traditional hospital services may increase admission rates, at least in the short or medium term.

4.6 Forensic Services in Wales

The Commission has been concerned about the level of forensic psychiatric services in Wales for a number of years. During the last 2 years, however, a well staffed medium secure unit has been provided at the Caswell Clinic in Mid Glamorgan in South Wales, and recently the Welsh Office has announced that a medium secure unit will also be provided in North Wales, and that the Caswell Clinic is to be enlarged. A medium secure mental nursing home, Llanarth Court, was opened early in 1993 in Gwent. The Commission welcomes these developments.

There are around 80 patients from Wales, mostly men, at the Ashworth Special Hospital, Liverpool. The hospital's distance from South and West Wales especially creates difficulties for relatives when visiting and also adds to difficulties in arranging aftercare. It is essential that a high security unit be provided nearer to the most populated areas of Wales. There is also a growing need for appropriate forensic services for people with serious challenging behaviour and mild learning disability.

Pennod 4
Y Comisiwn Yng Nghymru

4.1 Rhagarweiniad

Gan fod awdurdod Deddf Iechyd Meddwl 1993 a maes gweithgarwch y Comisiwn yn ymestyn dros Gymru yn ogystal â Lloegr, y mae'r Adroddiad Dwy-flynyddol yn ei gyfanrwydd yn berthnasol i'r ddwy wlad. Rhaid cofio er hynny am y gwahaniaethau rhwng y ddwy wlad o ran diwylliant ac iaith, ac hefyd o ran y modd y gweinyddir y gwasanaethau iechyd meddwl. Yng Nghymru gweinyddir swyddogaethau llywodraeth ganolog yn y maes hwn gan Ysgrifennydd Gwladol Cymru drwy'r Swyddfa Gymreig yng Ngaerdydd, a'r Swyddfa hon sy'n darparu adnoddau ar gyfer gwasanaethau iechyd meddwl drwy'r Awdurdodau Iechyd Dosbarth a'r Awdurdodau Lleol. Nid oes Awdurdodau Iechyd Rhanbarthol yng Nghymru. Ym 1989 cyhoeddodd y Swyddfa Gymreig ddogfen, 'Gwasanaethau Iechyd Meddwl – Strategaeth i Gymru", ac ynddi egwyddorion cynllunio clir, a "Cynllyn Iechyd Meddwl", sy'n gosod targedau penodol ar gyfer y gwasanaethau. Cyhoeddiadau pwysig eraill gan y Swyddfa Gymreig yw "Strategaeth Anfantais Meddwl Cymru Gyfan", (1985), sydd yn unigryw ac sydd wedi ennyn edmygedd cyffredinol (fe'i hadolygir yn flynyddol), ac "Adroddiad Grwp Ymgynghorol Cymru Gyfan ar Seiceiatreg Fforensig", (1992). Nid yw'r fenter Seisnig, y "Ffordd i Gynllunio Gofal ar gyfer Rhai Pobl ag Afiechyd Meddwl", yn berthnasol i Gymru — yma dilynir yn hytrach ganllawiau'r Strategaeth Iechyd Meddwl. Penodir deg o gomisiynwyr gan Ysgrifennydd Gwladol Cymru, ac y mae saith ohonynt yn perthyn i'r tîm sy'n ymweld â Chymru a Gorllewin Canolbarth Lloegr. Yn 1990 cynhaliwyd cynhadledd flynyddol y Comisiwn yng Nghaerdydd.

4.2 Y Comisiwn a'r iaith Gymraeg

O'r tua dau a thri chwarter miliwn o bobl sy'n byw yng Nghymru, gwell gan rhyw hanner miliwn, er eu bod yn ddwyieithog, siarad Cymraeg na Saesneg. Cydnabyddir pwysigrwydd yr iaith yn Neddf yr Iaith Gymraeg (1993). Y mae'r Comisiwn yn frwdfrydig dros ddarparu pamffledi Cymraeg sy'n esbonio hawliau cleifion o dan y Ddeddf Iechyd Meddwl a thros gyhoeddi Dull Gweithredu'r Ddeddf honno yn Gymraeg. Yn ei ohebiaeth ar faterion Cymreig, defnyddia'r Comisiwn bapur ysgrifennu dwyieithog ac y mae bob amser yn barod i ohebu yn Gymraeg pan fydd galw. Y mae pedwar o'r Comisiynwyr sy'n ymweld â Chymru'n siarad Cymraeg.

4.3 Y chwyldro araf yng ngwasanaethau iechyd meddwl Cymru

Dros gyfnod hir bellach bu newid graddol yn lleoliad a threfniadaeth gwasanaethau afiechyd meddwl yng Nghymru. Bu pwyslais cynyddol ar ddarparu triniaeth a gofal i gleifion yn agos at eu cartrefi, neu'n wir yn eu cartrefi, gan gyfyngu triniaeth a gofal ysbyty i achosion llym neu i grwpiau arbennig sy'n anodd eu trin ac nad yw'r gofal angenrheidiol yn cael ei ddarparu ar eu cyfer yn unman arall. Er bod datblygiadau tebyg yn Lloegr, llywiwyd a hybwyd hwy yng Nghymru gan Strategaeth a Chynllun y Swyddfa Gymreig. Un o'r canlyniadau mwyaf trawiadol yw fod dau ysbyty meddwl mawr, Ysbyty Gogledd Cymru yng Nghlwyd ac Ysbyty'r Parc ym Morgannwg Ganol, i'w cau yn ystod y ddwy flynedd nesaf.

O'r profiad o ymweld a gwasanaethau iechyd meddwl yng Nghymru a Gorllewin Canolbarth Lloegr dros y ddwy flynedd diwethaf, cafodd Comisiynwyr gyfle i sylwi ar rai o ganlyniadau'r chwyldro hwn. Nid oes amheuaeth nad yw'r newidiadau ar y cyfan yn dderbyniol gan gleifion, eu teuluoedd, a staff gwasanaethau. Maent yn cynnig gwasanaethau lleol, o fewn cyrraedd, gan leihau'r angen am driniaeth ysbyty. Gwelodd Comisiynwyr nifer o wasanaethau ardderchog yn y gymuned ac hefyd mewn ysbytai. Er hynny, carent dynnu sylw at rai pethau sy'n peri pryder. Mewn rhai ardaloedd y mae gwasanaethau annigonol ar gyfer y mwyaf anabl. Y mae hefyd bwysedd annerbyniol ar rai gwasanaethau llym.

4.4   Prinder adnoddau ar gyfer pobl ag afiechyd meddwl tymor hir

Mewn rhai ardaloedd, ymddengys fod mawr angen am wasanaethau preswyl a gwaanaethau dydd ar gyfer pobl ag afiechydon tymor-hir neu gylchol. I nifer gymharol fychan, h.y. y rhai hynny sy'n dioddef o anabledd enbyd, y mae angen am ofal trylwyr gan staff profiadol mewn unedau neu gartrefi a gynlluniwyd ar eu cyfer. Y math hwn o wasanaeth a geir ar hyn o bryd, er engraifft, yn yr ysbytai meddwl traddodiadol fel Ysbyty Gogledd Cymru ac Ysbyty'r Parc (a bydd yn rhaid sicrhau darpariaethau eraill ar eu cyfer cyn y gellir cau'r ysbytai hyn).

Mewn rhai mannau gwneir darpariaeth ragorol mewn unedau neu gartrefi y tu allan i'r ysbytai yn y gymuned ond heb ddarparinaeth lawn gall problemau enbyd godi. Daw Comisiynwyr ar draws aelodau o'r grwp hwn ar rai wardiau afiechyd meddwl llym. Fel arfer derbyniwyd hwy yno ar ôl iddynt gyflawni rhyw drosedd fechan, ar ôl ymddwyn yn od ar y stryd neu am eu bod wedi esgeuluso eu cyflwr corfforol yn ddifrifol. Derbynnir rhai i'r ysbyty o dan orfodaeth statudol. O dan ofal a thriniaeth mae eu cyflwr yn gwella, ond os nad oes darpariaeth arbennig ar gael iddynt, mae staff yr ysbytai'n aml yn teimlo'n anfodlon i'w rhyddhau a gall rhai aros ar wardiau llym am flwyddyn a rhagor mewn amgylchedd sydd yn anaddas iawn ar eu cyfer. At hynny, mae eu presenoldeb yn lleihau nifer y gwelyau sydd ar gael ar gyfer achosion llym ac y mae hyn yn achosi problemau mawr i'r unedau iechyd meddwl hynny (fel arfer mewn ysbytai dosbarth cyffredinol), sydd â phrinder parhaol o welyau. Os ydynt y tu allan i'r ysbytai maent yn achosi pryder mawr i dimau iechyd meddwl cymunedol. Y mae'r Comisiwn yn teimlo'n gryf y dylid rhoi sylw arbennig i sicrhau darpariaeth ddigonol ar gyfer y grwp hwn.

4.5   Pwysedd ar wardiau seiceiatrig llym

Barn y Comisiwn yw y dylai awdurdodau iechyd, wrth benderfynu nifer gwelyau a lefel staffio unedau meddwl llym, dalu sylw i ofynion presennol sy'n perthyn i'w hardaloedd hwy. Y mae rhai o'r unedau hyn o dan bwysau mawr, oherwydd prinder gwelyau, staff neu adnoddau cymunedol ac y mae hyn yn creu amgylchedd cythryblus, antherapiwtig a hyd yn oed annigonol ar brydiau. Er y gall gwelliannau yn y gwasanaethau cymunedol leihau'r cyfradd derbyn i ysbytai yn y pen draw, eto hyd nes y digwydd hyn, fe all y galw am welyau gynyddu oherwydd colli y gwasanaethau sy'n gysylltiedig â'r ysbytai meddwl traddodiadol wrth iddynt gael eu cau.

4.6   Gwasanaethau fforensig yng Nghymru

Bu'r Comisiwn yn pryderu am lefel isel y gwasanaethau seiciatrig fforensig yng Nghymru am nifer o flynyddoedd. Yn ystod y ddwy flynedd ddiwethaf, fodd bynnag, agorwyd uned diogelwch canolig, Clinig Caswel, ym Morgannwg Ganol ac yn ddiweddar y mae'r Swyddfa Gymreig wedi cyhoeddi y sefydlir uned diogelwch canolig arall yng Ngogledd Cymru. Cyhoeddwyd hefyd y bydd cartref nyrsio seiciatrig, sef Llys Llanarth, yng Ngwent yn 1993. Y mae'r Comisiwn yn croesawu'r datblygiadau hyn.

Ar hyn o bryd y mae tua 80 o Gymry yn Ysbyty Arbennig Ashworth, Lerpwl, y mwyafrif yn ddynion. Y mae'r pellter, yn enwedig o dde a gorllewin Cymru, yn creu anawsterau i deuluoedd sy'n ymweld â chleifion ac yn creu anawsterau ychwanegol wrth drefnu ôl-ofal i gleifion. Y mae'n rhaid darparu uned diogelwch uchel sy'n nes at ardaloedd mwyaf poblog Cymru.

Y mae angen cynyddol hefyd am unedau fforensig ar gyfer pobl sydd â gradd isel o anabledd dysgu ac ymddygiad heriol difrifol.

5.
VISITING THE SPECIAL HOSPITALS

5.1 Introduction

The three Special Hospitals — Ashworth, Broadmoor and Rampton, provide care and treatment for approximately 1600 patients who are detained under the Mental Health Act. Whilst the majority of patients are detained under Part III of the Act as the result of criminal proceedings, one fifth of patients enter by way of civil admission under Part II of the Act. The Commission has continued to pay frequent visits to the Special Hospitals and to meet periodically with the Special Hospitals Service Authority (SHSA) and with each of the Hospital Management Teams. (See Appendix 8 for the Commission's Special Hospital Visiting Policy).

In its Fourth Biennial Report the Commission warmly welcomed the appointment of four Commissioners to conduct an independent inquiry into complaints of improper care and ill-treatment of patients at Ashworth Special Hospital. Although their terms of reference required the Committee of Inquiry to focus primarily upon the situation at Ashworth, it is inevitable that many of their recommendations had important implications, not only for the three Special Hospitals and the SHSA, but also the Commission.

5.2 The Report of the Committee of Inquiry into Complaints about Ashworth Hospital

The Inquiry Report of the Committee was published in August 1992 and in relation to the Special Hospitals it has been the dominant event of the period under review. The Inquiry Report (HMSO: 1990) came to a series of disturbing conclusions about the regime at Ashworth Hospital and painted a vivid picture "of life in a brutalising, stagnant, closed institution". The Commission submitted extensive written evidence to the Inquiry and one former and three current members of the Commission gave evidence.

The Report made 90 recommendations, most of which were directed to those responsible for managing the hospital. It also made three recommendations about the Commission: that the Commission should no longer have the duty to investigate complaints; that the Secretary of State be empowered to direct the Commission to inquire into any matter which she thinks warrants investigation and, that the Commission should make suggestions for revising the Code of Practice to contain guiding principles on the rights of detained patients to be visited. Comment on the first two recommendations can be found in Chapter 16 and the third is referred to in Chapter 9.

The findings and recommendations sof the Ashworth Report have been the subject of extensive public comment and led, amongst other things, to the establishment by the Secretary of State for Health of the High Security Working Group under the Chairmanship of Dr John Reed. Publication of their report is understood to be imminent and further comment can be found at Chapter 10.

Whilst the implications of the Ashworth Report are primarily for those responsible for the hospital it is appropriate to consider the implications for the Commission. In the light of the Report the Commission did ask itself what it had been doing since its establishment to uncover and publicly expose the impoverishment of patient care identified in the Report. A useful starting point in analysing the Commission's role is to examine what it has said about the Special Hospitals in its first four Biennial Reports, since it came into existence in September 1983. At the level of management arrangements and policy-making within the hospitals, the Commission did at the outset make, in hindsight, some pertinent and pungent criticisms. For example, the absence of a complaints procedure in the Special Hospitals in the mid-1980's was severely criticised. It is undoubtedly true that pressure from the Commission was a major factor in the SHSA placing production of such a policy at the top of its agenda, shortly after it took over the management of the hospitals in 1989.

What is less satisfactory is the absence from the Biennial Reports of any really vigorous condemnation of the standard of patient care in some — if not all — parts of the hospital. There is criticism in the Fourth Biennial Report but it is very specifically focused and does not begin to match the appalling and distressing conditions disclosed in the Ashworth Report. This is, in part, a reflection of the difficulties that any outside organisation has in getting under the skin of a total institution, and thereby obtaining verifiable information that can justify trenchant public criticism.

From the beginning of its life the Commission recognised the danger that patients would come to see the Commissioners as just part of the "establishment" of the hospital. To a certain extent that has come to pass. More important, was the fact that Commissioners are often perceived as powerless in relation to the resolution of individual complaints from Special Hospital patients. There are many examples of the Commission successfully intervening in individual cases (as the Report acknowledges) but, overall, the Commission's ability to investigate complaints has been severely hampered by its resources, both manpower and financial. This matter was discussed in the Fourth Biennial Report (para 5.3). The burden of carrying out complaints investigations falls on part-time Commissioners who, apart from the limited training initiatives undertaken by the Commission itself, are untrained in the investigation of complaints. By contrast, the Health Service Commissioner has a full-time staff which does nothing else but conduct investigations in a thoroughly professional manner. Unlike the Health Service Commissioner, the Commissioners have no specific powers to assist them, other than the right to interview patients in private and have access to their records. The fact that the Ashworth Inquiry, armed with full statutory powers, legal representation and extensive public hearings, spent more than half its time getting to the bottom of four specific cases is an indicator of the difficulties encountered by the Commission.

The Commission is essentially a visitorial body. It is not an inspectorate, or not, strictly a complaints body adjudicating individual complaints. In its concern to fulfil its statutory functions towards individual patients' needs and their problems (many of them apparently trivial, but immensely important in the context of daily life in a closed institution) it sometimes did not adequately crystallise a more general view of the standard of patient care, about which it could give supportable public warnings. Commissioners often receive allegations from both patients and staff which the complainants did not wish to be carried through, ostensibly and sometimes overtly for fear that it would affect, for example, discharge prospects or result in staff reprisal. Since 1983 there have been two major changes in the management arrangements for the Special Hospitals, each of which was greeted with a perhaps over-optimistic expectation of the fundamental changes that would result. There was, undoubtedly, a reluctance amongst some Commissioners to publicly deplore standards of patient care because it might have been unhelpful in achieving fundamental changes which were being so sincerely proclaimed by the SHSA.

The Commission has many strengths. Its multi-disciplinary membership supplies a profound knowledge of how Special Hospitals work. Its wide experience of services for detained patients outside the Special Hospitals, provide a firm basis for more effective work in the Special Hospitals. The Commission has reviewed the way it visits Special Hospitals, and details of the steps taken to immediately enhance the Commission's visiting are referred to below (para 5.3). Its proposals for a more substantial reform of its composition and structure can be found at Chapter 16.

General Issues

5.3 Commissioners Visiting Arrangements

All Commissioners are expected to make a regular and substantial commitment to visiting the Special Hospitals and each is allocated to one of the three Special Hospital Panels (SHPs). The SHPs are divided into a number of multi-disciplinary teams, each of which is responsible for visiting designated areas of the hospital to ensure that the rights and interests of the patients are effectively safeguarded. Although the aim is to ensure that every detained patient in the Special Hospitals is contacted at least once a year, the Commissioners meet many of the patients much more frequently.

The visiting arrangements have recently been modified to increase the frequency of out of hours and unannounced visits. In addition, each SHP now has a core team of six to eight Commissioners who visit more frequently to monitor policy, procedures, standards of performance and other hospital-wide issues, including any matters which the visiting teams have identified as needing particular attention.

Following a successful trial at Rampton, a number of Commissioners in each SHP are now issued with keys when they visit. This development, which was welcomed by the majority of the staff, has enabled the visiting teams to move around the hospital more freely and without the need to divert hospital staff from their nursing duties to act as guides and escorts.

5.4 Patient Safety, Environmental Standards and 24 hour Care

In the Fourth Biennial Report (para 4.3(b)) reference was made to "slopping out" and the need to bring this

practice to an end at the earliest opportunity. It has generally welcomed the SHSAs intention to address this and a number of other deficiencies by way of a programme of environmental and care regime improvements. It has warmly applauded the partial introduction in some parts of the Special Hospitals of 24 hour therapeutic care and open access for patients to their rooms or dormitories at all times, and it looks forward to further progress being made in the future.

Despite these developments the Commission is aware that in many areas of the hospitals, the night staffing levels are very low (see para 5.14(c)). During the period under review, Commissioners identified the absence of any night alarm call systems in most of the rooms and dormitories into which patients are locked at night. It became clear to the Commission that in parts of the hospitals it would, in practice, be very difficult, if not impossible, for a patient needing urgent assistance to attract the speedy attention of staff. In the Commission's view this was wholly unacceptable and consequent upon urgent representations made to the SHSA and the Department of Health, assurances were given that all patients would have access to night alarm call systems by April 1994.

5.5 Transfer Delays

All previous Biennial Reports have reflected the Commission's grave concern about delays in transferring patients from Special Hospitals to Regional Secure Units (RSUs), local hospitals or community facilities. During the period under review the situation has not improved significantly. Many patients who have been identified by Patient Care Teams as suitable for discharge or transfer to less secure conditions, including some who have been granted a conditional discharge by a Mental Health Review Tribunal, continue to be expensively detained in an environment which is inappropriate to their medical and social needs.

The Fourth Biennial Report (page 21) announced the establishment of a working group to analyse transfer delays at Ashworth. The group, which completed its work in January 1992, confirmed the findings of previous studies that the delays are mainly due to external influences which include the multiplicity of organisations and individuals involved in the discharge and transfer process. Many cases take a long time to resolve simply because so many people are involved. Other reasons include a shortage of suitable places in RSUs, local hospitals and community-based accommodation, particularly for those who are homeless; a lack of specialist facilities for persons who are mentally impaired; funding disputes; poor communication and inadequate co-ordination amongst the relevant agencies.

The group also identified a number of factors specific to the Special Hospitals, including delays in the provision of contingent therapy or rehabilitation programmes; premature or inappropriate recommendations for discharge or transfer; changes in clinical personnel and other interruptions to continuity of care; and inadequate communications and avoidable delays in the internal administrative procedures. The working group's report, which included a number of recommendations for change, has been forwarded to the SHSA for further consideration and discussion.

Transfer delays will continue to be scrutinised by the Commission and the Core Team will take a particular interest in future developments. At Broadmoor a special task group has been set up by the Hospital Management Team to clarify responsibilities in relation to transfers and it is hoped that this will enable difficulties to be identified and resolved more promptly. It is encouraging to note that the appointment at Rampton of a liaison officer, with special responsibility for negotiating transfer placements on behalf of individual clinical teams, seems to have made a significant contribution to improving the situation.

On 31st March 1992 the number of Special Hospital patients recommended for discharge or transfer was 272. Of the 75 who had progressed to the full transfer list, 30 had been waiting less than 6 months; 23 had been waiting from six to 12 months; 15 had been waiting from one to 2 years and 7 had been waiting for more than 2 years. By 31st May 1993 the number of patients recommended for discharge or transfer had risen to 295 and 80 patients had progressed to the full transfer list; of these 34 had been waiting less than 6 months; 20 from 6 to 12 months; 19 from one to 2 years and 7 had been waiting to move for more than 2 years.

The Commission remains very concerned about the continuing delays and proposes that there should be a special review of those cases which have been on the discharge/transfer list for more than 6 months; that transfer delays should be a standing item on the agenda of all future meetings with the SHSA and Hospital Management Teams; and that the SHPs should continue to monitor the progress of individual cases in their respective hospitals.

5.6   Seclusion

The Commission welcomed the SHSA's initiative in setting up a group to review the use of seclusion within the Special Hospitals. The Commission was approached by the SHSA to nominate a member to this group and Mrs Shirley Turner, a former Commissioner, was nominated to sit in her personal capacity. The group has produced five discussion papers and in June 1993 Commissioners met with members of the group and publication of its final report and a new Seclusion Policy for the Special Hospitals is awaited.

In the meantime Commissioners have continued to accord the monitoring of seclusion a high priority on their visits. Those visiting Broadmoor have been concerned at the continued high level of seclusion, in particular the length of episodes of seclusion. Guidance in the Code of Practice often appears not be routinely followed and there has been a worrying increase in the number of episodes of self-seclusion, from 221 in September 1991 to 846 in December 1992, (as given in the Broadmoor seclusion returns). The Commissioners have also expressed concern at the quality of seclusion records. Seclusion forms are sometimes incomplete and reviews by the clinical specialist or Responsible Medical Officer (RMO) as required by the Code of Practice, are not always evident. There are still many instances of seclusion continuing when a patient is recorded as being "quiet and co-operative". The Orville Blackwood Inquiry Report identified just such a situation shortly prior to his death. Commissioners have requested the Hospital Management Team (HMT) to remind ward staff

that seclusion must not be used as a punitive measure and that any concern for the patient's physical health whilst in seclusion must be addressed urgently.

At the end of 1992 on the initiative of the Ward Managers, an innovative project was established to reduce seclusion on Abingdon Ward (the intensive care unit) at Broadmoor Hospital. Extra staff were allocated to the most disturbed patients which enabled them to be given free access to their rooms and to a small day room. This resulted in individuals leaving their rooms more often, giving the opportunity for more social interaction. Regrettably the project had to be curtailed because of financial restrictions.

Seclusion data provided by Broadmoor Hospital for the period 1st January 1992 to 31st December 1992 has been analysed. Whilst it is only possible to draw very limited conclusions from one year's statistics they do indicate several areas of concern:

a. There was no significant change in the number of patients undergoing seclusion throughout 1992. This is disappointing in view of the commitment of management to reduce it during this period.

b. There was no change in seclusion hours, except a very significant drop in average hours for female patients secluded on ordinary female wards. In the first quarter average hours per patient on the ordinary female ward was 79.1, and in the last quarter of 1992 the average was 18.9.

c. There remains a worryingly high number of episodes of seclusion in excess of three days on high dependency female wards and a significant number of episodes lasting over seven days. The Commission is concerned that such seclusion may well not comply with the guidance in the Code of Practice that seclusion is an emergency measure. This attitude is reinforced by the relevant provisions for recording seclusion in the hospital's current seclusion policy.

d. 7% of the seclusion episodes are described as self-seclusion and the Commission is aware that most will have arisen from requests by patients for privacy or bed rest rather than any need to actively seclude them. The revised Code of Practice at paragraph 18.15 states that the "Sole aim of seclusion is to contain severely disturbed behaviour which is likely to cause harm to others" and the Commission welcomes the Working Groups examination of this issue.

The data supplied to the Commission indicates that 6-9% of the seclusion episodes appear to contravene the Code of Practice as they are recorded as being implemented for the purposes of preventing self-harm or the threat of it. In addition, in one case a patient was secluded for concealing a lighter. This is punishment and clearly contravenes all existing guidance.

5.7   Women in the Special Hospitals

In the previous Biennial Report the Commission concluded that radical changes would be necessary within the Special Hospitals if women are to receive the type of care and treatment which they need to be able to build their lives after discharge. Since the publication of that report the findings of the Ashworth Inquiry have echoed and reinforced many of the Commission's concerns.

The Report deals elsewhere (para 5.2) with the response of the Commission to the Inquiry Report, but here it is important to note the separate attention given by the Inquiry to the care of women patients, and the fact that both research and action were called for to achieve change in the services available for these patients. Some changes have taken place, but the Commission feels that much still needs to be achieved in this area.

The Commission is concerned that the work of the working party established within Ashworth Hospital to develop detailed proposals for womens' services has had little effect. The Commission was invited to make an input to this group and commented on papers and proposals which it generated. It produced proposals for re-organisation based on a clear philosophy which took into account the needs of both staff and patients and regarded the proper recognition of such needs as essential if an appropriate therapeutic environment was to be created. This philosophy was not adopted and the re-organisation proposals which flowed from it have not been accepted.

A paper produced subsequently by the SHSA argued for the extension of integration of men and women patients on wards. This paper lacked sound research evidence to support its assertions about the benefits of integration for women and men. It also concluded that *"a person unable to contemplate moving to a mixed environment ... would most certainly be unfit for discharge"*. The Commission cannot support this statement. The SHSA produced a further paper on the subject of services for women patients in May 1993. This contained a list of principles which should guide the development of services, but did not provide a clear indication of how these principles would be translated into practice. The Commission was not invited to comment on either of these papers.

At the beginning of 1993 the Commission expressed grave concern about aspects of the care of female patients at Ashworth Hospital. As a result the SHSA established an external team to review services for women within the hospital. As this report goes to press, the Commission understands that the team has reported but that its report is not to be made public.

Within this period Commissioners have continued to receive serious complaints from women patients about their experiences, particularly within Ashworth Hospital. One complaint concerning a sexual relationship between a male member of staff and a female patient went to independent review, but the report was not accepted by the patient concerned and the Commission is continuing to pursue this case. One woman died whilst in seclusion and Commissioners have undertaken their own analysis of the care and treatment she was receiving. Another nearly succeeded in an attempt to hang herself. Commissioners are most concerned that this young woman's mental state has deteriorated whilst she has been in Ashworth and that her case is indicative of a failure to meet the needs of many of the women who are admitted.

It has long been recognised that women patients in Broadmoor Hospital have fewer amenities and are more greatly disadvantaged than men patients. This issue is now being addressed by the HMT in the context of the policy on equal opportunities. At present the women's wards have some of the worst environmental standards and access to parole facilities is far more limited than for men.

Commissioners have also for some time been concerned that women patients usually cannot consult a female doctor about physical health problems. At Broadmoor the HMT has been attempting to appoint female doctors for this purpose. The Commission feel strongly that it is the right of female patients to be examined by a female doctor if they so wish. A woman GP has now been appointed on a sessional basis. It also recognises the desirability of such patients having access to "well woman" clinics and annual medical screening.

The Commission continues to be concerned about the incidence of self harm amongst women patients in the Special Hospitals. Where patients exhibit this behaviour in response to mental distress, the Commission would like to see the further development of psychologically based strategies which would reduce reliance on the use of medication and, on occasion, seclusion.

5.8   Complaints

The Commission applauded the introduction by the SHSA on 1st April 1992 of a single Complaints Policy and Procedure applicable to all three Special Hospitals.

It is the Commission's view that primary responsibility for monitoring the complaints policy rests with the Special Hospitals, their Hospital Advisory Committee's (HACs) and the SHSA itself. The Commission has been consulted at length by the SHSA about its proposals to develop and refine the monitoring of the policy and the procedure and the Commission has been given unrestricted access to data arising from this activity. In addition it has been agreed that at regular intervals, the Commission will examine a random selection of complaints files in order to form a view as to how the policy and procedure is working. Reference has already been made to the difficulties experienced by the Commission investigating complaints in the Special Hospitals and it regards one of the principle objectives of the new policy as being to eventually ensure that most, if not all such complaints are competently handled within the Special Hospitals with the consequence that only a very few need to be referred to external agencies such as the Commission. Whilst it is too early to draw any firm conclusions it is pleasing to note that the number of complaints from the Special Hospitals to the Commission has declined in the period under review.

The Commission has submitted comments to the SHSA on its first experiences of the working of the policy and procedure. From the outset it was clear that the processing of complaints under the procedure presented the hospitals with a major administrative challenge, and the Commission was concerned as to whether sufficient resources had been allocated. Whilst it welcomed the time limits in the policy it has suggested that they may need to be reviewed as initial evidence indicated that some were unrealistic.

The Commission is aware that problems have been encountered in ensuring that complainants are regularly informed as to progress. The Commission has paid particular attention to the work of the independent investigators appointed under the policy and has noted a wide variation in the quality of their work. Deficiencies have been drawn to the attention of the SHSA. The Commission has continued to emphasise the importance of the findings and recommendations of the Ashworth Report concerning patient evidence and the assessment of its reliability as well as adequate training for all those involved in the handling of complaints. The Commission also commented on draft leaflets produced for both patients and staff about the complaints system.

The Commission warmly applauds the commitment of the Authority to ensuring that patients are fully aware of the complaints procedure and how to make the best use of it. The Commission hopes that the quality of complaints investigations will improve as the procedure itself is refined in the light of experience, and patients and staff gain confidence in its operation.

Given the sense of vulnerability experienced by patients in the Special Hospitals it is essential that rapid progress is made in increasing patients' confidence in the policy and procedure. Commissioners are not infrequently told by patients that complaining is ineffective and that they are fearful of repercussions should their complaints be formally pursued. A decline in such comments will be a true measure of the effectiveness of the new complaints procedures.

The case study set out on page 30 illustrates some of the difficulties encountered in investigating complaints in the Special Hospitals as well as the role of the Commission in ensuring the quality of Special Hospital investigations.

5.9   The Special Hospitals and Part IV of the Act

The patient's RMO has a responsibility to evaluate regularly whether or not a patient is consenting to his or her treatment. Should the patient withhold or withdraw consent or become incapable of giving valid consent, a second opinion from a doctor appointed by the Commission must be requested.

A detailed examination of compliance with the consent to treatment provisions of the Act on a number of wards at Ashworth Hospital revealed a disquieting state of affairs. Similar problems have been identified at Broadmoor Hospital (para 5.14(d) re: Orville Blackwood). At Rampton Hospital the consent to treatment provisions in respect of Forms 39 and MHAC 1 appear to work well, though Commissioners are concerned that Forms 38 are sometimes not being completed correctly.

The concerns of the Commission may be seen by clinicians as marginal and bureaucratic. However, the Commission is responsible for ensuring that requirements of the Mental Health Act are fully met and has anxieties about the nature of consent in closed institutions, where any perceived lack of compliance by patients can have serious consequences for them in terms of parole status and recommendations for rehabilitation and discharge.

The Commission expects staff to meet their statutory obligations. In the Commission's experience deficiencies in the documentation required by the Act often reflect a more serious failure to address the fundamental issues of human and civil rights about which the Act is primarily concerned. These difficulties have been discussed with the Special Hospital Services Authority and specific instances drawn to the attention of responsible medical officers. The response from the hospitals has not been encouraging and this reflects badly upon the professionalism of all concerned.

Over the two year period, the Commission has highlighted the following issues in the Special Hospitals:

a. Form 38 should be signed by the patient's current RMO. This function cannot be delegated to another doctor in the clinical team eg: senior registrar. Where there is a change of RMO it is the view of the Commission that Form 38 should be updated at the earliest opportunity.

b. The RMO should follow the guidance in the Code of Practice at Chapter 16.11. that *"the patient's RMO should personally seek the patient's consent to continue medication"*. The discussion should be recorded in the clinical notes.

c. When completing Forms 38, the Code of Practice guidance should be followed in that medication should be recorded on the form to show BNF categories, the route of administration and the dosage in relation to BNF dose range. Regular PRN or "as required" medication should also be included on the Form 38 if the patient is consenting.

d. Separate forms should be completed for ECT and medication, as they are different treatments.

e. It is the responsibility of the nurses administering medication to satisfy themselves that the treatment prescribed accords with the treatment plan to which the patient has consented. A copy of the Form 38 for medication should be kept with or close to the medication card so that the nursing staff can check the consent form prior to administering the medication.

f. The Commission is of the view that each time a new Form 38 or 39 is issued, the previous forms cease to have effect and that the only time it is possible to have two valid consent forms at the same time is when there is one for medication and one for ECT. Such consent certificates and photocopies should be clearly marked as cancelled. (Chapter 7)

The Commission regards its role in monitoring Part IV of the Act in the Special Hospitals as a crucial and integral part of the work undertaken by visiting Commissioners and will continue to accord it high priority.

5.10   Patients 'Advocacy and Patients' Councils

The Commission is pleased to note the considerable effort which is now being put into the development of patient advocacy services and Patient Councils at all three hospitals consequent upon the Ashworth Report Recommendations. The Commission's Chief Executive was a member of an advisory group established to consider the implementation of a patient's advocacy service at Ashworth Hospital and also contributed to discussions across all three hospitals about the establishment of Patients Councils. It is the Commission's view that the appropriate empowerment of Special Hospital patients, both collectively — so that they can effectively be consulted about issues relating to general policy as well as initiating their own contributions, and individually — so that patients can, for example, make effective use of the complaints procedure, can only be of benefit to the smooth running of the hospital.

5.11   Incident Reporting

The Ashworth Inquiry Report stressed the importance for both management and staff of being constantly aware of the patterns of patient behaviour and the efficacy of hospital regimes. They recommended the urgent establishment of a system of reporting all incidents (untoward events) however trivial. It was recommended that incidents should be classified according to their severity and that an incident review committee be set up.

The Commission is disappointed that it only limited progress has been made and would strongly urge that this matter is given high priority.

5.12   Hospital Advisory Committee (HAC)

Members of the HAC undertake the responsibilities of hospital managers under the Mental Health Act and their important duties include reviewing the detention of patients under Section 3 and 37 and monitoring aspects of the Complaints Policy and Procedure. Whilst the Commission remains concerned that the Code of Practice guidance about the manager's duty to review detentions is not fully complied with in any of the Special Hospitals, it has welcomed the progress which is being made in this area. At Broadmoor, Commissioners have welcomed the introduction of a new procedure under which patients are invited to meet with HAC members as part of the review of renewals of detention.

5.13   Ward Managers

The Commission has been pleased to observe that the introduction of ward managers is having a discernable impact at all three hospitals, as they become more involved and confident in their role. Both environmental and therapeutic changes are becoming evident in some parts of the hospitals. They have provided a useful focus for visiting Commissioners who have worked hard to establish a fruitful working relationship with them. It is clear that some ward managers have experienced frustration because of doubts about their authority to initiate change, particularly in the area of security. Some have encountered problems in persuading staff to adopt new and more enlightened approaches to patient care and treatment.

5.14   Individual Hospital Reports
Rampton
(a)   Patients with hearing impairment

Rampton is the Special Hospital which specialises in the care of patients with hearing impairment. Commissioners have continued to try to ensure that these patients are aware of and can exercise their rights under the Mental Health Act, and do not become isolated because of difficulty in communication. Recently Commissioners met with six hearing impaired patients in the education centre and the Commission hopes to continue this policy of meeting groups of such patients in an effort to identify their particular difficulties.

There is clearly a shortage of hospital staff skilled in communicating with patients who are hard of hearing and the Commission itself has acknowledged the need to recruit Commissioners with skills in this field. One Commissioner is currently undertaking a signing course.

(b)   Environment

The pioneering new regimes introduced into Moss Rose, Juniper, Firs and Maples wards whereby patients are afforded access to their own rooms and dormitories over 24 hours has been highly successful and the Commission welcomes its proposed extension to other areas. In the meantime Commissioners have continued to press for all patients to have access to toilet facilities during night time hours. At the same time the Commission has been pleased to note the hospitals' intention to fit all single rooms with privacy locks thereby enabling patients to control access to their own rooms, subject to a staff override.

Although the hospital is undergoing major alteration, it does not appear to be having a major effect on the patient activity. The Commission, has however, received a number of complaints from patients which suggests that the access to exercise and activity outside is difficult on some wards.

(c)   Staffing

Four Commissioners undertook an "out of hours" visit commencing at 11.00 pm one night, and 16 wards were visited. The majority of wards visited had only one member of staff on duty, although the acute wards and those operating the 24 hour therapeutic care had a higher staffing level.

Broadmoor
(d)   The death of Orville Blackwood

Orville Blackwood, aged 31, died in seclusion at Broadmoor Hospital on 28th August 1991. There were two inquests both of which returned verdicts of accidental death.

The SHSA established an Inquiry into Mr Blackwood's death. The Inquiry was also tasked with reviewing the death of two other Afro-Caribbean patients at Broadmoor in 1984 and 1988 in order to identify any significant common factors between the deaths. Its report (SHSA. 1993), published in August 1993, made

47 recommendations, many of which reflected those previously made by the Ashworth Inquiry.

The report made significant recommendations about the administration of medication in emergency situations; the use of Section 2 of the Mental Health Act; the use of seclusion and control and restraint techniques; the provision of adequate resuscitation training; the roles and responsibilities of RMO's and associate specialists; and the need for clear and humane procedures to be followed after the death of a patient. Many of the matters referred to in the recommendations have been identified by the Commission to the hospital in the past.

The report specifically addressed itself to racism in Broadmoor and determined that it existed in the hospital and that it was primarily a matter of staff attitudes. In a helpful discussion of racism in the forensic psychiatric system as a whole, and its affect on Broadmoor, it concluded, that whilst there was no problem of overt racist attitudes and literature, such as those revealed by the Ashworth Report, it was of a more subtle kind and generally was unconscious and not deliberate. Such racism was part of the background common to all three deaths and the report implies that, in some ways, it is harder to tackle than malicious and open racism. The Commission strongly supports the Inquiry's recommendations that a "root and branch" change in staff attitudes is required and it particularly welcomes the suggestion that a Senior Manager be appointed to tackle the problem of racism.

The reports recommendations will significantly influence the Commission's future agenda for its work at Broadmoor Hospital (and where relevant the other Special Hospitals) and progress on their implementation will be closely monitored.

(e)   Environment

During the past 2 years there has been significant improvement in the hospital environment with the commissioning of new wards and refurbishing of others. However, patients in the women's wards in Dorset House have very poor living conditions with inadequate bathrooms which provide little privacy and where basic standards of hygiene are difficult to maintain. Many patients arc still obliged to empty their chamber pot each morning. Commissioners welcome the decision to allow patients access to day areas at night on Berkshire Ward.

Commissioners also welcome the plans for the upgrading of all areas of the hospital and hope that these are completed on schedule. Refurbishment is causing disruption to the lives of patients and it will be important for this to be managed carefully.

Ashworth Hospital

(f)   Provision of medical services

The Ashworth Inquiry Report commented critically on the standard of medical services provided at Ashworth Hospital and recommended that the SHSA should consider how medical leadership at the hospital could be enhanced. The Commission is aware of the efforts currently being made to address these issues but it has to report that the standard of such services remains extremely variable with an unacceptable number of consultant vacancies. The resolution of these difficulties need to continue to be accorded the highest priority.

(g)   Rehabilitation

Commissioners have noted that the best use is not being made of the off-ward rehabilitation facilities of hospitals as they are not as freely available to patients as they should be. The frequency with which workshop activities and rehabilitation visits are cancelled because of staff shortages, is a matter of grave concern to Commissioners. In June 1993 Commissioners began systematically recording such restrictions and they will be pursuing the matter further. Lack of progress in improving access is particularly regrettable as Commissioners noted a number of important innovations in the rehabilitation programme — for example, the provision of car maintenance classes for women patients.

Case Study

THE INVESTIGATION OF A COMPLAINT OF ASSAULT BY STAFF

The complainant was admitted from Crown Court to Rampton Hospital under Section 38 of the Act in November, 1991 in order to assess his suitability for treatment under a hospital order. He was then 21 years of age.

In January, 1992 the Commission received a complaint from the patient that he had been physically assaulted by nursing staff on the evening of December 4 1991. He was initially attacked by another patient who was restrained by staff but broke away from them and began to attack him again. The complainant then threw a chair in the direction of the other patient which accidentally hit a nursing assistant involved in the restraint. The other patient was transferred to another ward whilst the complainant was placed in seclusion on the ward where he was reported to be regaining his composure and not threatening. However, later that evening he was visited by the nursing assistant who had been struck by the chair. He reported that the complainant was hostile and making threats to staff. The decision was then taken to transfer the complainant to another ward. He co-operated in the transfer but on arrival was placed in seclusion where he said he was assaulted by several members of staff including the nursing assistant hit by the chair. He sustained bruising about the face and other parts of the body as a result of this assault.

He returned to his original ward approximately three weeks later and shortly afterwards, as he had responded well to treatment, he was transferred to prison to serve out his sentence.

As the complainant had also complained to the Managers about this assault the Commission monitored the Managers' complaints procedure. The Managers reported the allegations of physical assault to the police and also instituted their own concurrent internal investigations into procedural matters relating to the complaint.

The police were not able to prosecute but drew the attention of the management to matters which should concern them. The Managers were not satisfied with the quality of their internal investigation and set up a second one which also concentrated on organisational and management issues. The report of this investigation was received in mid 1992.

At this stage the complainant had received no communication from the Managers about the outcome of their investigations into his complaint and, further, these investigations had failed to address the issue of physical assault since the police were not able to proceed. The Commission expressed grave concern at these failings and asked for a fresh and thorough inquiry into all aspects of the complaint.

In response the SHSA set up its own Committee of Inquiry into the complaint itself and also into the subsequent management handling of it. The Commission was provided with a copy of the full report of this inquiry at the beginning of 1993 but the complainant was only provided with those sections of the report relating directly to his complaint and not with the inquiry's findings on the managers' handling of it nor with the annexes to the report.

The central conclusions were that the Committee "...did not disbelieve his general allegation that an assault took place" but that "...he may have exaggerated the scale of assault. But even this cannot be proved." The report was critical of the quality of the two internal inquiries and the failure to communicate with the complainant.

Whilst acknowledging that the third report, by comparison with the first two, was a thorough and authoritative document, the Commission was critical of the reluctance to acknowledge in a direct manner some of the unpalatable conclusions which must flow from the inquiries disclosures. The reluctance to come to the inevitable conclusion that the patient's complaint was well founded was based upon the failure to elicit any direct supporting evidence of an assault but, as the Ashworth Inquiry advised, it is not essential that there should be corroboration of a patient's account.

Inquiry teams must weigh up all the evidence and decide where the probabilities lead them. As in this case the inquiry concluded that the complainant was not to be disbelieved it should have concluded that the assault took place and that it was by staff. The Commission also took the view that, on the evidence available to it, the Inquiry had no justification for concluding that the complainant may have exaggerated the scale of the assault.

The Commission concluded that the complainant is entitled to a full and unqualified apology in respect of both the assault and the failure to keep him informed and also to adequate compensation for his injuries and distress. He should also have been provided with a copy of the full report and annexes.

6.
THE INVESTIGATION OF COMPLAINTS

6.1 The Commission's Complaints Jurisdiction

The Commission's jurisdiction to investigate complaints is set out in Section 120(1)(b) of the Mental Health Act 1983. This section of the Act defines two types of complaint which are within the remit of the Commission's investigative powers; any complaint made by a person in respect of a matter that occurred while he was detained under the Act and which he or she finds has not been satisfactorily dealt with by the Managers of the hospital or mental nursing home; and any other complaint as to the exercise of powers or discharge of duties conferred or imposed by the Act in respect of a person who is or has been detained.

Despite the criticisms in the Ashworth Inquiry Report (Chapter 5) of the handling of complaints by the Commission it has continued to find this aspect of its work invaluable in reflecting and identifying issues of concern. Many are illustrated by the examples in this Chapter.

6.2 The Processing of Complaints

(a) Complaints Policy and Procedure

The majority of complaints are made by letter to the Commission office. others are brought to the attention of Commissioners when they interview patients on visits.

The Fourth Biennial Report (para 5.3) refers to the Commissions new Policy, Procedure and Guidelines for receiving and handling complaints. These have been revised and developed in the last two years with particular attention being paid to monitoring the timely handling and quality of complaints investigations.

A copy of the Policy is included at Appendix 9. This document together with the Procedure and Guidelines continues to be the main basis for the formal training of Commissioners and Commission staff who are responsible for handling complaints, and for monitoring the quality of Commission complaints work.

(b) Patients' fear of making complaints

Many patients present visiting Commissioners with statements about their experiences, which amount to complaints. Sometimes, especially but not exclusively in the Special Hospitals (see Chapter 5 for details of complaints investigations in the Special Hospitals), patients state that they would like to make a complaint but decide not to do so because of the fear of reprisals, loss of privileges, anxiety about antagonising the Responsible Medical Officer (RMO) or other members of staff.

The Commission hopes that as complaints' procedures are further developed and refined, and are better able to take such fear into account, patients' confidence in them will grow, and such reluctance will be reduced.

6.3 Statistics

In the period 1st July 1991–30th June 1993 the Commission received 1220 complaints. These compare with 1068 received between 1989–1991 and 1003, between 1987–1989. The figures indicate a continuing upward trend. The most frequent number of complaints remain in the categories of assault, medical care and services, medical treatment and transfer delays. The number of complaints about medical care and services has more than doubled. The number of complaints about transfer delays has dropped slightly.

Complaints have been received under all 17 categories. Statistical and other details can be found at Appendix 10.

The issues which are bought to the attention of the Commissioners range from the very serious to those which, though objectively not very serious, have a considerable impact on the welfare and quality of life of the detained patient concerned. In a break with past practice, a small sample number of Commission Complaints Investigations and their findings are reported at length in this Chapter. The cases selected illustrate a wide range of issues, many of which the Commission has encountered elsewhere.

6.4 Examples of Commission Investigations

(a) Case study 1

A complaint was made by a patient's mother through a Community Health Council, on behalf of her son, about his treatment whilst a patient at a local hospital. He had been admitted under Section 2 of the Act immediately followed by Section 3.

The complaint was about the following:-

i.   medication and side effects;

ii.   compliance with the consent to treatment provisions of the Mental Health Act;

iii. adequacy of information on legal rights given to the patient or his relatives;

iv.   implementation of detention power under the Act;

v.   difficulties in communication because of language problems;

vi.   adequacy of social work involvement; and

vii. the content and implementation of the patient's care plan.

In the course of its investigations all the patient's medical and nursing notes; statutory documentation relating to admission and consent to treatment under the Act and non-accidental injury records in respect of the patient were scrutinised. The patient, his mother and all relevant professional staff were interviewed.

The Commission in its adjudication upheld many of the complaints.

(i) Medication

The patient's mother complained that the increasing level of medication prescribed had not appeared to improve her son's condition. She was worried about the effects of the medication and concerned that possible side effects, such as constipation, lack of energy and "flat affect", should not be considered symptoms of an illness. She suggested that the increasing level of medication was not improving the patient's condition.

He was transferred to another hospital in October 1992 where his medication was reduced significantly as part of the standard assessment procedure there. By 25th November 1992 his medication remained considerably reduced. It was noted that this did not result in any increase in the patient's outbursts. He appeared more alert. Commissioners identified an inadequacy in the procedure for reviewing medication at the original hospital.

(ii) Consent to treatment and the Mental Health Act

Examination of the statutory documentation revealed that the patient had been treated in breach of the provision of Section 58(3)(a) of the Act for a month. This had occurred because the period the patient was on Section 2 had not been included in the hospital's calculation of the "3 month" date. It was also found that the patient's medicine card showed that he was being prescribed clopixol in excess of the British National formulary (BNF) limits, although his consent form (Form 38) referred to anti-psychotic medication within BNF limits.

Commissioners questioned whether the patient had given valid consent, as it was reported that he sometimes refused or spat out his tablets. He was reluctant to have injections because of fear of the needle. They concluded that there was sufficient doubt about the patient's ability to understand the nature, purpose and likely effects of the medication prescribed and also whether he had in fact consented, to have warranted a second opinion under Section 58 of the Mental Health Act by a doctor appointed by the Commission.

The patient's mother did in fact ask the hospital for her son to be referred for a general second opinion from another doctor. One was obtained from a consultant at another hospital who had close links with the patient's care team. He confirmed the patient's diagnosis and treatment. His opinion was not acceptable to the patient's mother, who did not consider it to be independent. The Commission concluded that it would have been desirable for the opinion to have been sought from a doctor not so closely linked with the team treating the patient. Had the provisions of the Mental Health Act 1983 been carried out there would have been an independent medical assessment of the patient's treatment plan by the doctor appointed by the Commission.

(iii) Provision of information as required under Section 132 of the Mental Health Act

The patient's mother complained that her son's legal rights under the Mental Health Act had not been explained properly to him or to her. She alleged that she had not received any information about her own or her son's rights, and in particular did not have any written information about her son's detention in her first language, Urdu. Commissioners discovered that the information had been sent to the wrong address as the hospital records were out of date even though the patient's mother was a regular visitor to the ward and ward staff were aware of her new address.

It was not until some time after his admission that an attempt was made to provide her with a letter in English and a patients rights leaflet in Urdu. By this time, however, the patient withheld his consent and the information could not be given.

(iv) Implementation of the powers to detain under the Mental Health Act

An inspection of the records revealed several irregularities in the use of the powers to detain the patient. The circumstances surrounding the patient's original admission under Section 2 suggested that this Section may have been used instead of a Section 3 only because the nearest relative was objecting to the patient's admission.

At the end of the patient's period of detention under Section 2, the patient was detained under Section 3. Both doctors providing the medical recommendations were approved by the Secretary of State under Section 12 of the Act but neither of them knew the patient. He was not seen by his RMO or GP. The Commission concluded that this was bad practice as it was not an occasion where the urgency of the situation prevented the involvement of a doctor who knew the patient.

Subsequently his detention under section 3 was renewed by a locum registrar under Section 20 of the Act; a power that can only be exercised by the patient's RMO.

When the patient was transferred to a second hospital, the requisite statutory transfer documents were not received from the transferring hospital.

The Commission concluded that for a period of his detention the patient was unlawfully detained.

(v) Communication

The patient's mother complained that her limited English had caused difficulties in her communications with her son's care team and that there was a failure to provide an independent interpreter. The staff had different views about her ability to communicate in English. Some had concluded that she had sufficient ability and cited two letters from her to the hospital in English to confirm this. These letters were in fact written, with the help of the Asian women's Resource Centre, and did not therefore provide reliable evidence of her ability to communicate in English.

Whilst it was clear from the records that some attempt was made to provide interpreters, too much reliance was placed on the patient's father who was formally separated from his mother. Where interpreters were provided, too often it transpired that Urdu was not their first language.

The Commission found that proper and vigorous consideration had not been given to the provision of competent interpreters. It specifically expressed its concern about the use of the patient's father as an interpreter on a number of occasions. The report of the Commission's adjudication referred to paragraph 2.35 of the Code of Practice, which indicates that approved social workers

(ASWs) and doctors should receive sufficient guidance in the use of interpreters, and that Local and Health Authorities and Trusts should make arrangements for there to be an easily accessible pool of trained interpreters.

(vi) Social Work involvement

The Commission found little evidence of active social work involvement in this case. The work undertaken was limited to that required to prepare reports for Tribunals and Hospital Managers hearings.

(vii) Care Plan

The patient's mother questioned the content and benefit of her son's care plan. The Commission in fact commended the detailed care plan, and the time and consideration devoted by all relevant hospital staff to its preparation. It was noted however, that it did not incorporate any strategy to engage the patient's mother or family. The Commission concluded that this was an omission in this particular case.

(b) Case study 2

A patient died whilst an in-patient detained under Section 3 of the Mental Health Act.

He suffered induced epileptic fits caused by an obsession with drinking water (polydipsia) which reduced his sodium level. Following a fit on 10th January 1993 he died, choking on his vomit in the presence of nursing staff.

The patient's mother complained to the Commission that:

i. her son's continuing care was not of a sufficient standard to prevent the events which killed him;

ii. provision of a varied and therapeutic care plan was not in place;

iii. there was a lack of adequate communication between the involved medical staff and the patient's parents about specific aspects of their son's clinical condition and management.

The Commission was informed that the relevant health authority (as purchaser) intended to institute an inquiry and that an inquest would be held. The inquiry report found -

i. that the patient's care plan, "had been continually adapted and updated to take into account his changing circumstances ..." and that the care plan in operation throughout his stay was appropriate in balancing the inevitable risks associated with providing the patient with the quality of life which both he and all around him sought to secure; and

ii. that "There had been a number of areas of concern ..." about the patient's management on the night of his death and that appropriate action had been taken.

(i) The patient's care

The patient's mother wrote to the Health Authority expressing dissatisfaction with that part of their report about her sons care plan, and the management of specific aspects of his condition. She copied her letter to the Commission.

Two Commissioners interviewed the patient's RMO, clinical medical officer and the charge nurse. A Commissioner also attended the inquest at which there was a finding of "lack of care".

The Commission concurred with the conclusions of the Health Authority inquiry that there were deficiencies in the care provided on the night of the patient's death in that -

i. inadequate information had been given to the night staff nurse in charge of the ward about the patient's current state and the clinical plan;

ii. the staff nurse had not followed the medication and treatment plan as directed;

iii. adequate monitoring and appropriate intervention had not been made into the patient's behaviour in the hours before his death;

iv. the staff nurse and nursing assistant lacked knowledge about the availability of specific relevant medication (ie rectal diazepam): and

vi. there was an apparent lack of competence in resuscitation techniques amongst the night staff.

In respect of the patient's ongoing treatment whilst at the unit, Commissioners accepted that his care plan was appropriate, but found that more effective monitoring of the patient's fluid in- take should have been undertaken. It also suggested that greater efforts might have been made to reduce the patient's cigarette consumption, a possible potential factor in water retention. They were most concerned that the nursing staff did not appear to have been made fully aware by senior medical staff of the potential risks of excessive drinking, leading to water intoxication. Better informed night staff could have resulted in improved monitoring and intervention, and alerted nursing staff to the importance of reporting increased symptoms.

Despite instructions for weekly electrolyte assays to be undertaken, this was not implemented. Measurement of fluid intake was undertaken for a short period but the records were lost.

The Commission was gravely concerned by the apparent lack of medical supervision and involvement to ensure that instructions were implemented, and by the loss of the fluid intake records.

The Commission concluded that the consultant should have considered a more active intervention policy to restrict the patient's fluid intake after he suffered his first fit, either by bringing in additional nursing staff (which had been agreed in principle) to "special" him, or moving him to a side ward where observation could have been more effectively undertaken.

It found that the patient's clinical plan was not effectively implemented or modified to reflect the patients increasingly serious clinical condition.

(ii)   Therapeutic care plan

A range of alternative therapeutic activities was in fact identified in the care plan, but implementation was haphazard, despite the best efforts of the nursing staff. In part, this was a consequence of the patient's schizophrenic illness and the problems experienced in identifying activities in which he could be persuaded to become involved. The Commission noted that the patient mix on the ward, which consisted mostly of elderly patients, may have resulted in reduced staff observation of this young disturbed patient.

(iii)   Communication

The Commission was concerned that when the patient's mother tried to complain to medical staff about her son's treatment she was immediately referred to the Unit Manager.

The Commission expects, particularly following an acute episode, that it should be routine for medical staff to discuss the situation informally with the complainant, before referring him or her to management.

The Commission made a number of recommendations in its report, the majority of which have been accepted. These included :

i.   improved clinical records;

ii.   a detailed procedure to improve communication at nurse handover;

iii.   a review of the junior doctors' induction programme; and

iv.   in the event of complaints about medical care treatment initial discussion with the complainant at consultant level should be part of any formal complaints procedure.

(c)   Case study 3

On a recent scheduled visit to a hospital Commissioners saw a young woman who complained about the manner of her admission to hospital. While at home she had been allocated a Community Psychiatric Nurse (CPN). On one particular day she was visited at home by her GP, social worker and consultant psychiatrist. An application for her admission to hospital for assessment under Section 2 of the Act was completed. As she was disturbed, police assistance was summoned. The young woman alleged the police presence was unnecessary. She thought that the force used was disproportionate and that she was not given time to get her personal belongings together. She was handcuffed and transported to hospital in a police car, flanked by police officers.

Commissioners met with three members of the Hospital Management Team. They requested the following actions:

i.   that the patient be given every assistance should she wish to complain about the behaviour of the police;

ii.   that the Management Team inquire into the circumstances surrounding the patient's admission and consider whether it could have been handled differently; and

iii.   that the Management Team establish why this patient was transported to hospital in a police car rather than an ambulance.

The complainant's version of events was fully corroborated by the excellent nursing entry in the care plan, which detailed the events surrounding her admission. The patient's RMO, in his letter to her general practitioner prior to her admission, had indicated that she should be transported by ambulance. It is the Commission's view that when a seriously disturbed, mentally ill patient needs to be conveyed to hospital, in almost every case, an ambulance should be used. Guidance to this effect is contained in the Code of Practice. They found that the police involvement had been unnecessary. As the patient had a community psychiatric nurse it would have been desirable for them to be involved.

(d)   Case study 4

The patient made a formal complaint to the Managers of a London hospital that she was indecently assaulted after midnight in the female dormitory by a newly admitted male patient. She received a written response to her complaint from the senior nurse manager. His letter stated that all three members of staff on duty on the night in question "were accounted for". They had been engaged with other professionals in admitting the patient. He apologised that the incident had occurred. He noted that, as a result "the patient concerned was moved to another ward", and that "a member of staff is stationed at the far end of the ward throughout the night".

The patient was not happy with the response, she wrote back to the senior nurse manager questioning whether her experience of assault resulted from a failure in the procedures when her assailant was admitted. She apparently never received a reply to this letter.

The complainant wrote to the Commission asking for the following matters to be investigated:

i.   that the indecent assault should have been prevented by staff, who she stated were "lax and reckless" in dealing with the situation;

ii.   that her complaint had not been taken seriously.

The Commission carried out a full investigation.

It found the patient's account of the incident convincing. It did not conflict with the circumstantial evidence, and nothing came to light to cast doubt upon it.

The Commission was concerned that the assault was not recorded in the incident book. The Commission recommended that the Hospital Managers investigate why it was omitted. It found that the incident records were badly kept, with some items tippexed out, inadequate descriptions of actions and outcomes, and, in some cases, no entry at all in these columns. It recommended that the recording of incidents needed to be reviewed as a matter of urgency.

The Commission found it unacceptable that a person should be subject to attack whilst a patient on a psychiatric ward. It recommended that, where there are mixed wards, and where patients are not able to lock their rooms, Hospital Managers must ensure that there are enough staff on duty to observe the doors to the dormitories.

The Commission recommended that an admission procedure should be available on every ward. Good admission procedures and staffing policies should ensure that a situation does not arise where there is no available member of staff available to attend the other patients on the ward and immediately respond to such incidents.

The Commission noted that little support was given to the patient by the night staff and there was little acknowledgement of her distress.

In respect of her allegation that her complaint was not properly dealt with by the hospital, the Commission concluded that the hospital's Complaint's Policy was inadequate and had not been adhered to. The Commission recommended that it should be revised as a matter of urgency. The letter sent to the patient did not fulfil the requirement to keep her fully informed of the progress and the outcome of the hospital's inquiries. The statement that "all three staff were accounted for" was not an answer to her criticisms. Neither did the statement that the patient, who committed the assault, had been moved to another ward, acknowledge that he remained a regular visitor to the ward where the incident took place.

6.5 Complaints against Commissioners and the Commission

Over the past two years, four complaints against Commissioners were received and dealt with under the relevant Commission policy and procedure (Appendix 11). One complaint was upheld, another partially upheld and a third was not upheld. The fourth complaint was withdrawn by the complainant. The Commission regards its complaints against Commissioner policy and procedure as one of its quality assurance measures and strives to improve its service as a consequence.

The Commission has been the subject of a complaint to the Health Service Commissioner. The complaint concerned the impartiality and fairness of its handling of a complaint about aspects of the complainants detention under the Act. Whilst the complaint was not upheld, the Health Service Commissioner made a number of important comments, which are currently being considered by the Commission.

7.
CONSENT TO TREATMENT

7.1 Introduction

The Commission is responsible for the administration of the Consent to Treatment provisions of Part IV of the Mental Health Act and these make heavy demands on all concerned with their implementation.

7.2 Section 57

(a) Type of referrals

All referrals of patients to the Commission under Section 57 were in relation to psychosurgery. There were no referrals in relation to hormone implantation. The majority of psychosurgery operations continue to be undertaken in the Geoffrey Knight Unit at the Brook Hospital in London.

(b) Statistics

The total number of patients referred to the Commission in the period under review (01 07 91–30 06 93) was 46. This number is significantly lower than in previous years (1989-91 65, 1987-89 52, 1985–87 54, 1983-85 57). This is largely attributable to the problems Brook Hospital experienced in the latter half of 1991 in obtaining supplies of yttrium rods. It is too early to determine whether the new purchaser/provider arrangements are having any effect upon referral patterns.

The main centres specialising in the work covered by Section 57 are given in Table 1:

Table 1

Brook Hospital	38
Pinderfields Hospital	4
Atkinson Morley's Hospital	3
University Hospital of Wales	1
Total Referrals	46
Certificates issued	42

Table 2 shows the gender of referrals.

Table 2

Gender of referrals	
Male	15
Female	31
Total	46

Table 3 refers to the centres and operations currently available in England and Wales.

Table 3: Operating Centres and Types of Operationss Performed during Period of the Biennial Report

Operating Centre	Nature of Operation
Brook Hospital	Stereotactic Subcaudate Tractotomy
Pinderfields Hospital	Stereotactic Bifrontal Tractotomy
Atkinson Morley's Hospital	Limbic Leucotomy
University Hospital of Wales	Bilateral Anterior Capsulotomy

A new operating centre in Dundee, Scotland has recently been established which performs stereotactic anterior capsulotomy. This centre is outside the jurisdiction of the Mental Health Act 1983.

(c) Referrals from outside the jurisdiction of the legislation

There are few centres throughout the World which undertake psychosurgery, consequently a number of referrals are received each year from countries outside England and Wales. The registered medical practitioner, the nurse, and the third professional whom the Commission team meet when they visit the patient are from the hospital where the operation is to take place and will not have known the patient for very long nor will they be involved in the follow-up and aftercare.

When two referrals were received from the Republic of Ireland, the appropriate Health Authorities paid for the team of three people appointed by the Commission to visit the patients and meet with the professionals at the referring hospitals. The opportunity to visit patients in their own enviornment was most beneficial and in future the Commission will be inviting similar responsible Authorities abroad to make the same arrangements.

(d) Aftercare

The whole question of the provision of aftercare following psychosurgery has been recognised by those undertaking the work as an important component in achieving the optimum response in some patients. It is a matter of concern to the Commission that often little attention has been given to plans for aftercare by the time the patients capacity to consent is being assessed by the appointed persons.

(e) The third consultee

The issues which arise in relation to Section 58(3)(b) (para 7.16) apply to assessment under Section 57.

(f) Section 61

Under Section 61 of the Act the RMO is required to provide a report to the Commission on behalf of the Secretary of State. The report should be submitted 6 months after the operation. In approximately a quarter of the cases no reports have been provided at all. Those submitted have varied substantially in their comprehensiveness. A systematic review of these reports and the associated procedures is currently being undertaken.

(g) Form 37

If the operation is postponed for more than two months after certification it is the view of the Commission that a fresh certificate is required as the person's clinical condition and consent status may have changed in the interim.

(h) Consent over time

The Commission was asked for its advice about a patient who went into a coma for periods of time. The issue which arose was whether, having consented to the operation, that consent continued to be valid if the patient lapsed into coma again before the operation could have taken place. The view of the Commission was that, provided this eventuality was considered at the time of the original consent then it remained valid. Legal advice obtained by the Commission subsequently supported this view.

(i) Delegated consent

One patient asked to delegate consent to her husband for him to make the decision whether she should undergo psychosurgery. Legal advice was sought and the Commission concluded that delegated consent did not fulfil the requirements of the Act and that patients must consent themselves.

7.3 Section 58

It remains a matter of profound concern to the Commission that responsible medical officers (RMO's), Mental Health Act administrators and managers are still finding it difficult to comply with the requirements of Section 58 of the Act. For example, in one hospital a doctor who was approved under Section 12 was completing consent forms on behalf of the RMO on the mistaken assumption that approval under Section 12 was equivalent to appointment under Section 58. The Commission expects that the RMO, defined in the Act as the doctor in charge of the patient's treatment, will be the Consultant in charge of the case, who is formally responsible for documenting consent to treatment provisions. On those occasions when the Consultant is not immediately available, the Commission expects that there will be another doctor of Consultant status acting as deputy.

7.4 Demand for "Second Opinions"

A detailed analysis of numbers of requests for second opinions is given in Appendix 12. Since the previous Biennial Report, there has been a marked increase in the number of "second opinions" under the provisions of Section 58. While it may be that some of the increase is more apparent than real — as a result of possible under-recording during the process of centralisation — there is evidence that there has been a true increase, based upon the statistics collected over the last two years, though the pattern of requests in terms of sex, age and type of treatment is little changed.

The Commission has no control over the number of requests received and is under a statutory obligation to identify a medical practitioner appointed to provide a statutory second opinion when requested to do so. Some of the increase may be due to growing awareness of the importance of the need for clearly defined legal authority to impose treatment on patients who are either unable or unwilling to give consent. There is also some evidence that there is an overall increase in the numbers of patients being compulsorily admitted but the findings of a recent research study (**Bean** 1993) suggests that centrally collected statistics are not a reliable source of information. (see 18.2(b)).

7.5 Availability of Second Opinion Appointed Doctors

Since the previous report, the Commission has reviewed the procedure for appointing doctors under the provisions of Section 58. The monitoring procedure (para 7.6) also provides information relevant to the renewal of appointments. It has been evident that the work is very unevenly distributed, with some second opinion appointed doctors (SOADs) undertaking a disproportionate number of visits often to the same hospital. Procedures have been instituted to distribute the work more evenly. However, availability and the constraints of geography sometimes make this difficult to achieve.

7.6 Monitoring

The arrangements for scrutinising the reports of Second Opinion Appointed Doctors now also includes scrutiny of the form authorising treatment (Form 39) since appointed doctors provide a copy of this report to the Commission. This has enabled the Commission to take remedial action where consent to treatment certificates have been inaccurately completed and/or are invalid. More frequently the monitoring group identifies some technical deficiencies in the description of the treatment plan which are subsequently drawn to the attention of the appointed doctor.

7.7 Anti-psychotic Medication

Treatment plans are usually described in terms of the drug categories recorded in the British National Formulary. the Commission has been concerned about reports of polypharmacy and of medication being given in doses substantially higher than that generally recommended by the British National Formulary. While the Commission itself cannot set limits to treatment, the recording procedure requires appointed doctors to pay particular attention to these issues in the exercise of their clinical judgement. Appointed doctors are now being asked to record the treatment plan with a limitation on the number of drugs in each category which can be prescribed. The same principles apply to the very much larger number of certificates issued for patients who are consenting to treatment under the provisions of Section 58(3)(a). These consent forms are examined by Commissioners on their hospital visits.

7.8 Agreement between Section 58 Appointed Doctor and the RMO

The form now used by appointed doctors to report back to the Commission indicates whether the treatment plan has been changed following the consultation between the RMO and the appointed doctors. This appears to happen infrequently but some significant changes do occur, particularly where ECT is proposed.

7.9 Ethnic Issues

a. The SOAD report form requests information on the ethnic background of the patients and this has been subject to some systematic study (**Fennell** 1993).

b. The perception of many black patients is that a disproportionate amount of high dose medication is prescribed to them, partly because of racist stereotypes of dangerousness. Many black patients perceive all doctors as being influenced by these stereotypes and they therefore have little faith in the effectiveness of Section 58 in preventing unnecessary medication.

7.10 Section 61

Problems have continued in relation to the small number of patients who remain in hospital sufficiently long to come within the provisions of Section 61. As a result the Commission is to re-design the report form (MHAC 1) and to circulate again to managers an outline of the section requirements, already clearly set out in the Code of Practice. The infrequency with which patients outside the Special Hospitals are subject to these reports in part explains the lack of familiarity with the provisions of this section. The Commission is reviewing the procedure for the scrutiny of Section 61 reports to determine when further second opinions should be arranged.

7.11 Cancellation of Consent Certificates

The need to update consent forms identified in the Fourth Biennial Report (para 6.11) has not generally been acted upon. It is therefore suggested that the statutory documents, Forms 38 and 39, should include the words *"This certificate renders earlier certificates null and void"*.

7.12 Emergency Treatment and Section 62

The Commission remains concerned about treatment given in emergency situations which fall outside the Consent to Treatment provisions of the Act. Some treatment is described as being given under the provisions of Section 62 when in fact the patient is either not detained or is held under the short-term holding powers of the Act to which Section 62 does not apply. The Commission is also aware of emergency treatment being given to disturbed patients by relatively unskilled staff under the common law. Such treatment falls outside the Commission's statutory responsibilities, but the Commission urges that a careful audit be undertaken of such treatment and invites the Royal College of Psychiatrists to extend its study on homicides and suicides* to include the deaths of patients being treated in emergency situations.

* See Note 1 at end of chapter

7.13 "As required" Medication

The Commission draws attention to treatment which is to be given as required or on a "PRN" basis. On some occasions this treatment will be clearly within the terms of the consent forms signed by the RMO under the provisions of Section 58(3)(a) (for example if the patient occasionally requests night sedation). On other occasions this medication is written for use in emergencies where consent either may not be secured or certainly cannot be anticipated. Where the need for emergency treatment recurs the Commission feels that this treatment should be incorporated in the authorization provided by a Second Opinion Appointed Doctor, even if the patient generally consents. Where the treatment is given under the provisions of Section 62 it must be systematically recorded. In this connection it should be noted that many hospitals still have not instituted an effective recording system for Section 62 treatment, as recommended by the Code of Practice, particularly when this involves medication. The Commission will, in due course, publish a Commission Practice Note about this.

7.14 Code of Practice

The new Code of Practice came into force on 1st November 1993. This recommends the RMO certifying the patient's consent on Form 38 to indicate the dose range of medication used and also to ensure that the validity of Form 38 is reviewed at regular intervals and that a new form is completed if the patient continues to consent. Form 38 should be formally reviewed at least once a year and the patient's medical notes should contain clear evidence that this has occurred.

7.15 Nurses and the Consent to Treatment Provisions

The Commission has not noted any improvement in the awareness of nurses as to their responsibilities in administering medication which falls within the provisions of Section 58. The Commission will shortly publish a Commission Practice Note for the guidance of nurses. It has also been in touch with the United Kingdom Central Counsil for Nursing Midwifery and Health Visiting to urge that the relevant information be included in their guidance.

7.16 Statutory Consultees

It is the responsibility of the RMO to identify the third person who meets the statutory requirements. Difficulties previously recorded in identifying the third person professionally concerned with the patient's medical treatment have continued and this remains a major source of difficulty for Appointed Doctors when undertaking second opinion visits. Indeed, these difficulties have increased as services have become more dispersed and localised. The Commission has considered the problem of interpreting the statutory requirement, an issue which has not yet been tested in the courts. It has concluded that to require the statutory "other" consultee to be invariably professionally qualified and included in a professional register would be unnecessarily restrictive. At the same time, the Commission has grave doubts about the validity of some certificates which, for example, refer to the "Ward Clerk", "Gymnasium technician" and "Occupational Therapy Aid".

The Commission suggests that the appointed doctor should endeavour to meet with somebody whose qualifications, experience and knowledge of the patient should enable them to make an effective contribution to the work of the multi-disciplinary team. Appointed doctors are at liberty to consult with other members of staff if this is seen as helpful and this may include those not professionally qualified but who are working under the supervision of a qualified person who takes responsibility for their actions and whose name will therefore appear on the statutory form. The responsibility of managers to ensure that the appropriate personnel are available for consultation is outlined in paragraph 16.33 of the Code of Practice. The Commission has in the past drawn up a list of staff who can act as the third person; these include a social worker, occupational therapist, clinical psychologist, physiotherapist, pharmacist, chaplain, dietician and art/music therapist.

7.17 Out of Hours Service

Further study has been undertaken as to the feasibility of providing guidance and access to an appointed doctor outside usual working hours at weekends and bank holidays. The study which was based upon requests made on an answering machine indicated that there was little demand for such an extension.

7.18 Appointment of SOADs

There have been instances of serious misunderstanding about who is entitled to provide second opinions under the provisions of Part IV of the Act. In one hospital, a consultant who was approved under Section 12 of the Act as having special experience in the diagnosis in the treatment of mental disorder completed "second opinions" for a colleague, and then contacted the Commission to ask for the appropriate fee. This doctor had not been appointed under the provisions of Section 58 and therefore these certificates were invalid. On another occasion an appointed doctor was asked directly by a hospital to provide a certificate for a patient. It should be noted that an appointed doctor is not formally appointed until approached by the Commission with respect to a specific patient.

7.19 Clozapine (Clozaril)

A Commission Practice Note outlining the Commission's views on the haematological monitoring involved in the administration of this atypical anti-psychotic drug has now been published and has been generally welcomed.

7.20 Anorexia Nervosa

A Commission Practice Note on the treatment of patients with Anorexia Nervosa whose condition warrants detention, a very small minority of all those who are receiving treatment, will be published shortly.

7.21 Description of Treatment

The Commission remains concerned about the difficulties which RMOs have in describing treatment in the terms required by Section 58. Many consultants continue to write treatment plans in specific terms rather than using the categories of drugs given in the British National Formulary (BNF), fail to record clearly the doses to be given or the route of administration and include medication and treatment not subject to the provisions of Section 58(3)(a) and (b). On occasions the wrong category of drug is given. For example, Clopixol Acuphase which is an anti-psychotic drug with an extended action and classed in the BNF under "Anti-Psychotic Drugs" (4.2.1) is often recorded as an anti-psychotic depot injection (4.2.2) on the certificate, and therefore authorised as such. These issues are considered in new advice to Second Opinion Appointed Doctors shortly to be made available, which takes into account the revised Code of Practice. Elements of this advice will also be available for RMO's. One major concern of the Commission is that there should be a detailed description of the patient's capacity to give valid consent in their case notes, where the RMO has decided that a Form 38 is appropriate. Frequently there is no documentary evidence in the clinical record of the patient's consent status.

7.22   Access to Health Records Act

The Commission has considered the implications of the Access to Health Records Act 1990 and concluded that the Consent to Treatment certificates, the appointed doctor report form and any private records maintained by a appointed doctor or appointed person would fall within this Act. To date no requests for disclosure have been received by the Commission.

7.23   Drugs not in the BNF

From time to time new preparations are approved by the Committee on the Safety of Medicines and made available to consultants before they appear in the BNF. It has been accepted that medical practitioners may prescribe such drugs, although the patient needs proper and relevant information as to the status of the drug being recommended if their consent is to be valid. Doctors involved in providing "second opinions" have endorsed treatment with drugs not established in the BNF specifying the drug by name and recording the upper limit of dosage which has been approved.

7.24   ECT

The Commission has suggested that where there is a break of more than 3 weeks in a course of ECT treatment authorised by a SOAD, the certificate should be regarded as lapsed and a further second opinion sought if the patient is not able to give valid consent under the terms of Section 58(3)(a). There remains no formal mechanism for cancelling Consent to Treatment certificates but RMO's are asked to note the three week rule as an issue of good practice.

Of the certificates authorising treatment examined by the Commission, 46% were for authority to prescribe electro-convulsive therapy. The majority of patients who receive this treatment suffer from severe depressive illnesses associated with loss of insight, many are elderly and the most frequent single indication for this treatment is that the patient is refusing to eat or drink as a result of their depressive illness. The reports of the appointed doctor frequently indicate that in their view the treatment in these circumstances is "life-saving". However, the Commission has no means of collecting systematically any data on the outcome of treatment so administered except to note that the small number of deaths of detained patients notified to the Commission rarely involve patients who have been receiving ECT

under the provisions of Section 58. Because such patients do not usually remain in hospital long enough for their detention to be renewed, the provisions of Section 61, whereby the Commission receives a report on progress, do not apply. The Commission does not have the resources to follow up each course of such treatment, though this would clearly be a valuable source of information about what is seen by some as a controversial treatment.

7.25   Scrutiny of section papers

To ensure that the certificate issued by an appointed doctor is valid, the appointed doctors are asked to scrutinise the statutory documents relating to admission, that is, the application and the medical recommendations. The new Code of Practice suggests that they should examine the primary copies of these documents, or photocopies (in which case the primary copy should be available for reviewing by the appointed doctor if he requests). On a number of occasions appointed doctors have identified errors in the documentation which have rendered the detention unlawful and have notified the managers so that steps can be taken to inform the patient and if possible to rectify the errors.

7.26   Consent to Treatment in the Special Hospitals

(see Chapter 5).

NOTES

1."The Confidential Enquiry into Homicides and Suicides of Mentally Ill People", Royal College of Psychiatrists

REFERENCES

Bean P. (1993), The Nature and Extent of Compulsory admissions to Mental Hospitals within the four London Regional Health Authorities—Report to the Kings Fund.

Fennell P (1993), Treatment without Consent: The operation of the Second Opinion Procedure in Section 58 of the Mental Health Act—Report to the Nuffield Foundation.

8.
THE REVIEW OF DECISIONS TO WITHHOLD PATIENTS' MAIL

8.1 Powers of Managers to Withhold Patient's Mail

The Commission has a statutory duty under Section 121(7) to review decisions at the Special Hospitals to withhold postal packets. The Managers of a Special Hospital may withhold outgoing mail if they consider that the postal packet is likely to cause distress to the addressee or anyone else (other than a member of the hospital staff) or is likely to cause danger to any person. These decisions which are subject to review by the Commission at the request of the patient are routinely monitored by visiting Commissioners. If the addressee has made a written request to the RMO, the Managers, or the Secretary of State that mail from any detained patient should not be forwarded, the withholding of mail is not subject to review. This applies both to patients detained under the Act in Special Hospitals and patients in other hospitals. Incoming mail may also be withheld from Special Hospital patients if, in the opinion of the Managers, it is necessary to do so in the interests of the safety of the patient or for the protection of other persons. Such decisions must be reviewed by the Commission at the request of the patient or the person who sent the packet. The Commission has a power to direct that the item of mail or any part of its contents should not be withheld. The Commission's procedure in relation to this statutory responsibility can be found at Appendix 14.

8.2 Rampton Hospital

The procedures followed at the hospital appear to work well with all the necessary notifications being strictly observed and the Commission is generally satisfied.

8.3 Ashworth Hospital

Commissioners visiting Ashworth have been concerned about the procedures operating in the hospital, for the following reasons:

(a) They have become diverse because prior to unification different procedures operated in Park Lane and Moss Side Hospitals.

(b) Various departments including security, medical, and administrative are involved in the procedure.

In July 1993 Commissioners urged the hospital to standardise its procedures and produce a policy/procedure document. A new policy has now been drafted under which decisions about the withholding of mail will be devolved to ward level. Commissioners were particularly concerned to discover that there was no central register of withheld mail and that patients were not always told why their mail had been withheld.

Mental Health Act information leaflet number 13 advises patients of their right to inform the Commission in writing if they wish to appeal against a decision to withhold mail. Patients have complained that they have not been provided with the Commission's correct address and therefore were unable to seek a review by the Commission.

8.4 Broadmoor Hospital

The Commission has been concerned about a lack of clarity in implementing the hospital's procedures for monitoring patients mail.

9.
MENTAL HEALTH ACT CODE OF PRACTICE

At the beginning of 1990 the Secretary of State asked the Commission to monitor the implementation of the Code of Practice and to advise Ministers of any changes to the Code which the Commission thinks appropriate. During the past two years the Commission has received many letters from mental health professionals seeking clarification of points of the Code and identifying issues of concern which could or should be covered. As a result of their visits to hospitals, members of the Commission have also highlighted parts of the Code which required revision.

The first report to Ministers on the monitoring of the Code of Practice was submitted in January 1992. The report made proposals for revisions of the Code to eliminate errors and to amend parts of the Code which had proved difficult to interpret. The Department of Health consulted widely on the changes proposed. A second report was submitted to Ministers in September 1992.

A revised Code of Practice was produced by the Department of Health on behalf of the Secretary of State in early 1993, laid before Parliament on 19 May 1993 and came into force on 1 November 1993. The main changes in the revised Code are as follows:-

(a) Chapter 2

Assessment: clarification of admission criteria under the Act.

(b) Chapter 9

Nurse's holding power: changes to encourage the sound practical application of this emergency measure.

(c) Chapter 15

Medical treatment: a re-ordering to make it easier to follow, with greater emphasis on the need for monitoring of the implementation of treatment plans.

(d) Chapter 16

Medical treatment and second opinions: a number of changes and additions to clarify the Second Opinion Appointed Doctors arrangements, associated patient records and improved information for patients.

(e) Chapter 18

Patients presenting particular management problems: the Mental Health Act Commission has carried out a comprehensive review of this chapter in the light of observations it has received and also its own monitoring. The Commission has particularly examined the adequacy of current guidance on the difference between security, taking control of an emergency, and restraint. The proposed changes are intended to clarify the differences.

(f) Chapter 19

Psychological treatment: changes include an improved definition of such treatments and clear guidance on the use of 'time out'.

(g) Chapter 20

Leave of absence — Section 17: some changes are made to assist understanding of Section 17 and the procedures for its use.

(h) Chapter 24

Duties of the hospital managers: additional guidance on how they should be carried out in NHS Trusts and registered mental nursing homes.

(i) Chapter 26

Aftercare: updated to include appropriate reference to the Care Programme Approach.

(j) Chapter 29

Children and young people under the age of 18: updating in relation to the Children Act 1989 and relevant case law.

There is a range of smaller but significant changes to other chapters.

The revised Code does not conflict with the principles on which the existing Code is based but rather expands, clarifies and updates the guidance it contains.

In 1993, the Commission began to identify specific performance targets for aspects of the Code with the aim of providing purchasing authorities with guidance on monitorable standards which can be incorporated into future contracts with provider units. The overall objective is to raise the quality of practice in relation to the Act. The Commission intends to consult widely with relevant authorities before issuing guidance notes on such standards.

10.
SERVICES FOR DIFFICULT AND OFFENDER PATIENTS

10.1 Introduction

The Fourth Biennial Report (at page 36) welcomed the establishment of the Steering Committee of the Review of Health and Social Services for Mentally Disordered Offenders and others requiring similar services (The Reed Committee). Its final summary report was published in November 1992. Amongst its recommendations were the establishment of two further Department of Health working groups to examine the provision of high security psychiatric care and also the care and treatment of people with psychopathic disorder. At the time of going to press publication of their reports was imminent. In addition the Mansell Report (Mansell) on the services for people with learning disabilities and severely challenging or offending behaviour has been published. The period under review has therefore been one of considerable activity in relation to the making of policy recommendations; the Reed Report makes 276 recommendations, a reflection perhaps of the serious inadequacies in the current service which have been identified repeatedly in previous Biennial Reports.

The response so far from Government can be summarised as follows:

a. The identification of the needs of Mentally Disordered Offenders in the Health of the Nation - Mental Illness Key Area Handbook (Department of Health 1993).

b. The identification in the NHS Planning and Priorities Guidance for 1994/1995 of the needs of Mentally Disordered Offenders as a first order priority.

c. The appointment of a National Advisory Committee on Mentally Disordered Offenders.

d. The provision of extra capital funding for medium secure provision.

e. The provision of pump priming monies for court diversion schemes. (para 10.5).

In more practical terms, the number of prisoners transferred to hospital has almost doubled in 2 years, from 325 in 1990 to 611 in 1992. Such progress is to be warmly welcomed, but it is clear there is a very long way to go before all the issues set out in previous Biennial Reports are effectively addressed.

10.2 The Reed Report

The Commission has welcomed the majority of the 276 recommendations made in the Report. The Commission's Chief Executive and Commissioners have participated in a number of conferences throughout the country promoting the principles and recommendations of the Report. The Commission particularly endorses the Report's five guiding principles that mentally disordered offenders should be cared for:-

a. With regard to the quality of care and proper attention to the needs of individuals.

b. As far as possible, in the community, rather than in institutional settings.

c. Under conditions of no greater security than is justified by the degree of danger they present to themselves or to others.

d. In such a way as to maximise rehabilitation and their chances of sustaining an independent life.

e. As near as possible to their own homes or families, if they have them.

The Commission recognises the importance of a set of guiding principles around which the wide range of mental health and criminal justice agencies which are involved in the delivery of health care to mentally disordered offenders can unite.

The summary report stresses that a "substantial" development of services in accordance with these principles cannot be met within existing resources and that the capital cost is likely to be in the region of £71 million, together with annual revenue costs of £63 million. The Report suggests that 1,500 medium secure places nationally will be required, with upwards of an additional 2,800 staff in all disciplines. Although a target of 1000 places was established in 1974 (Glancy 1974) it has never been met and the current number of medium secure hospital beds stands at around 650.

The Commission welcomes in particular the decision to include within the final Summary Report presented to Parliament all the recommendations made in the discussion paper on racial and cultural issues published for consultation by the Department of Health and the Home Office (1992), especially as this paper reiterates many of the points made in the Commission's submission to the Joint Steering Committee chaired by Dr John Reed.

The Commission strongly supports a number of observations made in the Report, namely, that endorsement by the Government of the guiding principles is essentially a re-affirmation of "long standing policy"; that the widespread agreement about the recommendations of the Report are a "helpful base from which to move forward"; that "practice all too often falls a long way short of what is desirable"; and that "things must certainly move more quickly than they did after the Butler and Glancy Reports".

The Summary Report concludes with a quote from "The Great Gatsby":

"It eluded us then, but thats no matter — tomorrow we will run faster, stretch out our arms further . . . "

The challenge presented by the Reed Report is that all those involved in the delivery of care to mentally disordered offenders do not miss the excellent opportunity for improving such care and that we do not in the final words of the same novel " . . . *beat on, boats against the current, borne back ceaselessly into the past".*

The Report, which was primarily concerned with assessing how services should be delivered to mentally disordered offenders, contains some recommendations about existing legal provisions. The Commission has given further consideration to how Part III of the Act might be amended to bring its provisions more in line with the overall policy objectives of the Report. Any amendment requires the careful balancing of the conflicting interests of individuals and society. It is clear that Part III of the Act needs to be reviewed in the light of Reed and in the Commission's view the following questions need urgent attention:

(a) Remand to hospital for reports and treatment (Sections 35 and 36)

Should section 35 be broadened so as to duplicate a Section 2 order with its primary purpose being the assessment and, as necessary, treatment in an appropriate setting of persons suffering from mental disorder, rather than the preparation of a court medical report?

Should persons remanded to hospital under Section 35 be excluded from the compulsory treatment provisions in Part IV?

Is it appropriate that if a person is charged with murder, for which the penalty is fixed, a court may remand him to hospital under Section 35 but, if the medical report indicates he requires treatment, the court has no power under Section 36 to return him there to receive the treatment he needs?

Is the limit of 12 weeks for Section 36 remands sufficient, particularly when time awaiting trial exceeds that period and continued treatment may be needed?

(b) Transfer to hospital of remand prisoners (Section 48)

Following the introduction of the Criminal Procedure (Insanity and Unfitness to Plead) Act 1991, should the provision which permits courts to impose a restriction order on Section 48 patients in their absence, without trial or conviction, or any right to trial upon recovery, be repealed?

If an RMO considers that a patient no longer requires treatment, is it appropriate that where he furnishes a report to that effect to the court the patient may be remanded in custody or on bail but, if the report is sent instead to the Secretary of State, the accused must be returned to custody?

Should the Home Secretary be precluded as a matter of law from transferring patients to mental nursing homes (ie. private hospitals) under Section 48?

(c) Sentencing

Should Section 38 include provision for an interim guardianship order and, where a court is satisfied that a hospital order is required but unclear as to an offender's dangerousness, an interim restriction order?

Is there any merit in empowering magistrates to impose a full hospital order without trying or convicting an accused person, but not allowing them to impose an interim hospital order where they are satisfied that he or she did the act with which they are charged?

Is it proper that a restriction order may be founded upon medical examinations conducted some months previously and that the oral evidence required before it

is imposed can be furnished by a practitioner who is not approved under Section 12?

Should courts be empowered in appropriate circumstances to require a purchaser or the Department of Health to designate a hospital for a defendant's admission?

10.3 The Future of High Security Psychiatric Care

High security psychiatric care in England and Wales is provided by the three Special Hospitals: Ashworth, Broadmoor and Rampton (see Chapter 5). These hospitals contain approximately one quarter of all patients detained on any one day under the Mental Health Act and the Commission devotes a considerable percentage of its resources to monitoring the operation of the Act in these hospitals. The Commission therefore has a very special interest in the future provision of the care they currently provide.

The problems experienced in delivering high security psychiatric care in the Special Hospitals have been set out in previous Biennial Reports and are also referred to in this report (Chapter 5). Amongst the more serious is the mis-location of patients. Recent research (Maden et al 1992) suggests that up to half of the current population, including the majority of women patients, may need services other than in conditions of high security. Of this group 80 per cent were regarded as requiring medium secure care whilst 3 to 6 per cent were judged not to require hospital care at all. Transfer delays (Chapter 5) remain a major problem. High security care is not provided in a vacuum and the problems referred to above result in part from inadequacies elsewhere in the system. There is undoubtedly a need for substantially more medium secure places (especially long term medium secure accommodation), but it should not be forgotten that, in addition to the one in four Special Hospital patients who currently move on to medium secure care, one in seven return to prison, and about one in three move directly back to the community.

In tackling problems of high security care attention has to be paid to the health and social care systems to which it must relate. The professional, administrative and geographical isolation of the Special Hospitals remains a profound problem. (Chapter 5) Whilst the Commission does not wish to speculate about the recommendations of the High Security Working Party it certainly hopes that the following general proposals will be vigorously addressed:

a. That the provision of high security psychiatric care should be dispersed and provided in units which in terms of size and design are more suited to the provision of individual care.

b. That high security psychiatric care be integrated into general health provision by way of integration at an appropriate level into the purchaser-provider relationship. The Commission sees no reason why high security care cannot be provided by NHS Trusts. Whilst it may be necessary for there to be an interim central purchaser because of the relative lack of experience in this field amongst purchasers, in the medium term the Commission envisages such responsibility passing to main-stream purchasers.

c. That competent multi-agency assessments of the true need for high security psychiatric care be implemented as soon as possible. Until this is identified there will continue to be a serious mismatch between need and provision, which at an individual level can result in detriment to the health of patients, deprivation of their rights, and a gross breach of the guiding principles set out in the Reed Report. Transfer delays are a significant example of such a consequence.

10.4   Transfer Delays

This matter is dealt with in Chapter 5 of the Biennial Report.

10.5   Diversion of Mentally Disordered Offenders from the Criminal Justice System

The Commission welcomes the support of the Reed Committee for the principle of diversion of mentally disordered offenders from the criminal justice system. At the same time it recognises the many practical problems involved.

More than "pump priming" will be needed if diversion schemes are to be preserved, to develop and to become an established feature nationally. The participation of psychiatrists and social workers needs to be written into contracts and job descriptions.

There is an advantage in a diversity of schemes, the requirement of inner city areas, for example, being different from elsewhere. The avoidance of unnecessary remands to prison for assessment, and the expediting of hospital admission for those already in prison, are different tasks from the identification of mentally disordered people in police custody and the Crown Prosecution Service's exercise of its powers to discontinue prosecution in appropriate circumstances.

Calls upon the probation or social services to respond promptly to the needs of candidates for diversion impose demands which are not always easy to meet. Courts already find difficulty in securing hospital placements for some urgent cases. A recent Magistrates Court case notified to the Commission involved a 21 year old woman charged with causing criminal damage to motor cars. Having re-offended while on police bail she was remanded in custody to Holloway Prison. Her solicitor recognised that she was suffering from a mental disorder and the court agreed she should be remanded to hospital under Section 35. The local NHS Trust was unable to offer a bed as was the nearest hospital in an adjoining district. It was only the personal intervention of the Chairman of the Bench, who also happened to be one of the Mental Health Act Managers of the latter hospital, which resulted in the patient's immediate admission. Subsequently, the court proposed placing the woman on a probation order with treatment conditions. A place was found for her at the nearby hospital, but they would only accept her once confirmation of an extra contractual referral had been received from her own health district. The court was advised that this would take a week to process and therefore felt obliged to remand her back to Holloway for that period. Again the personal intervention of the Chairman resulted in her being admitted immediately.

10.6   Provision for People with Learning Disabilities and Challenging Behaviour

Many people with learning disabilities and challenging behaviour may be subject to detention under the Mental Health Act. They may present a challenge to either community or hospital services and are often picked up by the police for questioning or detention.

The Reed and Mansell Reports make important recommendations about the care of this group. Of particular concern to the Mental Health Act Commission are those who are assessed, for purposes of the Mental Health Act, as mentally impaired or severely mentally impaired. These legal categories include those with a significant or serious impairment of social functioning associated with abnormally aggressive or seriously irresponsible conduct. (Section 1(2), Mental Health Act 1983)

People with severe mental impairment have been cared for in residential settings and do not often come to the attention of the police or the courts. The implementation of community care will, however, increase the number of people with severe impairment living in the community and at risk. Individual special provision is essential and the Commission supports the Mansell Report recommendations for individualised, small, community based services which are sufficiently comprehensive to meet the needs of people with learning disabilities.

The case of D which was notified to the Commission illustrates the failure of community services to meet individual needs. D is 21 years old, and has severe mental impairment with limited language and communication skills. He attended a special school until he was 16, when he was transferred to a residential school run by a voluntary organisation. Between the ages of 16 and 19 he committed a number of offences including acts of indecency but was not charged by the police. When he was 19 he returned to live with his parents in London. His sexual problems and difficult behaviour continued; the day centre he attended could not meet his needs; and there was no effective intervention. When he was 20 years old he assaulted a policewoman in the street, was charged with sexual assault and attempted murder, and was remanded to Brixton prison where he was segregated and as a result became increasingly upset and disturbed. He was finally committed to hospital under a hospital order and transferred to a private secure hospital. There is no immediate prospect of appropriate community care being provided for him.

Some people with mental impairment have a moderate impairment of intelligence but a serious impairment of social functioning and possibly a personality disorder. Many people in this group come to the attention of the police and the courts and the safeguards, provided under the Police and Criminal Evidence Act 1984 and its Codes of Practice are important.

Their diversion from the criminal justice system may be important in some cases, but in others court proceedings and sentencing may be necessary to ensure their long term care whilst under sentence. Some may have acquired damaged personalities which, coupled with a degree of learning disability, makes them more vulnerable to mental illness and the commission of minor offences. Clinical intervention can often be provided during the course of a sentence or probation order.

The case of P illustrates some of the problems. He is 19, has a moderate learning disability, and lives at home with his parents. He now has no day service and no further education because of funding difficulties. He has been in trouble with the police, has been charged with criminal damage, breach of the peace and burglary, has been given two conditional discharges, and has been made the subject of a probation order. P needs a safe, supportive environment. On one occasion he was held in police custody for two nights with no access to an "appropriate adult" (as required by the PACE Codes of Practice) nor did he have access to a lawyer.

The Mental Health Act Commission monitors the use of detention in hospital for people with learning disabilities and is very concerned about the implementation of joint policies for aftercare planning and the operation of court diversion schemes. The Principles and the practice guidelines set out in the Mansell Report provide a framework for the provision of appropriate social care for people with learning disability in the community, particularly those who have challenging behaviour.

10.7 Section 136 of the Mental Health Act

The Commission has continued to pay attention to the role of the police in psychiatric emergencies in public places, and in particular, the implementation of Section 136 of the Act which was identified as being of key importance by the Reed Committee.

(a) Choice of place of safety

Paragraph 10.5 of the Code of Practice leaves the location of places of safety to local agreement although the Home Office has suggested that hospitals are preferable to police stations. Persons detained at a police station have additional rights under the Police and Criminal Evidence Act, including the right of access to legal advice. Experience suggests, however, that the environment of some police stations is unsuitable for the detention of mentally disordered people in custody especially when prolonged. Mental Health facilities located neither in a hospital nor a prison are preferable. However, providers are not always able to produce suitable venues. The only available places may be far from the urban centres where police contacts most often occur and may not be readily accessible to Approved Social Workers (ASWs) or local mental health teams. It is inappropriate for assessments to be carried out on a ward before it is known whether admission is appropriate, and it is not good practice to carry out assessments in busy accident and emergency departments that have no suitable room for the purpose. Some hospitals find difficulty in handling violent individuals during the period of assessment before they are sectioned and before anti-psychotic medication can be given under Mental Health Act powers. An agreed policy should attempt to identify those cases which should be taken to a police station rather than a hospital.

There have been occasions when police, called to a disturbed individual in an Accident and Emergency Department, have declined to use Section 136 on grounds that it is not a public place.

The Commission encourages the provision of specialised Section 136 assessment units set up in suitable premises and locations and urges purchasers to include such provision in contracts.

(b) Placement following assessment

Delays in admission may occur when there is no vacancy at the hospital where assessment has taken place and a bed has to be sought elsewhere or, in cases where the person concerned has no fixed abode, a local Trust provider declines to accept responsibility. There is a danger that appropriate use of the Act may be discouraged.

When detention under the Mental Health Act is found to be unnecessary social services should be able to provide assistance such as transport home or to a hostel. Some hospitals complain that police who deliver Section 136 cases do not stay until the assessment has been completed and then are not available to help remove patients who are not admitted. On the other hand, the police have problems with undue delay by hospitals in commencing assessments and inappropriate reliance on them for the provision of transport.

(c) Implementation of Section 136

In theory, the officer on the spot should decide whether to invoke Section 136 and remove the person as swiftly as possible to an agreed place of safety. The legality of the common practice of taking prospective patients to a police station en route to hospital needs clarification, but it may be unavoidable in the following situations:

i. when the judgement of the arresting officer needs to be confirmed by a superior;

ii. when the initial arrest may be for an offence and only later, while being transported to, or while at the station, may mental disorder be suspected.

The Police and Criminal Evidence Act makes provision for arrested suspects thought to be mentally disordered. An "appropriate adult" (eg. a relative or mental health worker) should be asked to attend the police station and an examination by a police surgeon should be arranged. Assessments with a view to sectioning can, of course, take place on persons detained other than under Section 136.

Note: The 72 hours allowed for assessment begins at the time of arrival at the "place of safety".

The Commission welcomes the establishment of agreed policies and ongoing liaison between police, health and social services on the implementation of Section 136. It commends trusts that have already developed detailed specifications for the roles and responsibilities of all concerned, established systematic monitoring of incidence, duration and outcome of assessment and provided for the needs of those not admitted to hospital. ASWs need to be available to respond at any hour to calls for Section 136 assessments. A nationally agreed record form for all Section 136 assessments would facilitate analysis of varying practice. Training in all procedures relevant to psychiatric emergencies in public places should be part of basic training for police as well as for social workers and other mental health professionals. At present avoidable confusions still occur, for example, in the meaning of "public place" and "appropriate adult" and in the procedures for entering private premises for the purposes of Section 135.

REFERENCES

1. Department of Health/Home Office (Reed J (1992)) Review of Services for Mentally Disordered Offenders and others requiring similar services — HMSO London.

2. Department of Health (Mansell J L (1993)) Services for People with Learning Disabilities and Challenging Behaviour or Mental Health needs

3. Department of Health (Glancy J E (1974)) Health Service Circular (Interim Series) 61

4. Malden et al (1992) Treatment and Security needs of Special Hospital patients

11.
MENTAL HEALTH SERVICES FOR PEOPLE WITH LEARNING DISABILITIES

11.1   Introduction

Commissioners visit hospitals for people with learning disabilities where there are, or are likely to be, detained patients. They also encounter people with learning disabilities in mental illness services, and take an interest in those under guardianship in the community.

Monitoring of availability of hospital places suggests some slowing down in the rate of hospital closure, though this is not universally the case. The severity of disability of those who remain in hospital, together with revenue problems and falling land values are factors which contributed to the reduced closure rate.

11.2   Service Provision

The Commission is concerned that adequate provision should be made for that small minority of people with learning disabilities who fall within the provisions of the Mental Health Act. Commissioners have found that policies in this area are sometimes unclear or unsatisfactory, often relying on distant private sector provision, unsuitable institutional provision, or the use of community provisions which lack the appropriate staffing and facilities. Services primarily designed for people with mental illness may prove to be unsuitable in terms of both staff expertise and facilities, and often leave people with learning disabilities isolated and vulnerable amongst other patients.

The very nature of learning disabilities means that their care must include help in acquiring adaptive social behaviour, communications and independent living skills. The model of care offered must include a prominent social education dimension. Services are commonly under- resourced in respect of appropriate therapeutic and educational provision.

11.3   Special Hospital Provision for People with Learning Disabilities

With the occasional exception only two of the Special Hospitals take patients with a primary category of learning disability (mental impairment/severe mental impairment). Most of these patients are in Rampton Hospital, with smaller numbers in Ashworth Hospital. The numbers are declining, and new admissions have fallen dramatically in recent years. There are major problems in providing appropriate care for this diminishing group. Transfer delays can be unacceptably long. In some cases, staff from the Special Hospital service who know the patient could helpfully spend time with that patient in a new setting, helping them to settle in.

11.4 The Reed and Mansell Reports

These two major reports (Chapter 10) both discuss the provision to be made for people with learning disabilities and severely challenging or offending behaviour. Although the reports were written in parallel, and there were links between them, they do not seem to be wholly consistent in their views on the scope for reliance on small domestic settings and mainstream mental health services.

The Commission urges that the implementation work now in hand should take into account, the wide range of support required, including short-term assessment, treatment and long-term support. Attention also needs to be paid to the need for high staffing levels, to the importance of training not only for the staff who only specialise in this work but also for those who only occasionally work with people with learning disabilities.

It is vital that the development of new services should be closely related to identified needs, and monitored for effectiveness. Services which only partially meet the identified needs will mean that patients suffer from an inappropriate level of security and may be located far from their home areas. There is a heavy responsibility on purchasers to define and adequately fund the services required, and on providers to develop and maintain a level of knowledge and skills which enables them to meet the needs of service users and the expectations of purchasers. If people are to have an appropriate service as their needs change, there must be an adequate range of flexible resources. Effective monitoring and the development of good practice is essential.

11.5 Advocacy

The Commission has been pleased to encounter a number of advocacy schemes. These schemes have on the whole been found to be enriching and enabling in the lives of patients. Generally they do not appear to have created undue problems for staff although they have generated an appropriate level of constructive tension which, if handled sensitively, can be a benefit to patients, staff and service providers. Some financial and organisational difficulties have been encountered in sustaining advocacy schemes over an extended period.

The Commission's experience is that successful advocacy schemes are likely to:

a. Be independent of the hospital.

b. Have a clearly defined role.

c. Provide orientation and support for volunteers.

d. Allow time for a relationship between advocate and patient to develop naturally.

e. Be well publicised among staff.

f. Be backed by procedures for debating and, where possible, resolving conflicts which inevitably will arise between advocates and institution.

11.6 De Facto Detention

Hospitals sometimes have difficulty protecting the civil and human rights of people with learning disabilities who are not detained under the Act, but whose liberty is restricted for safety reasons. Commissioners continue to emphasise the importance of having clear and well-publicised policies on the restriction of patient movement. Such policies should be based on the principles of minimum restriction and maximum support, stimulation, and opportunity. Staff should also consider using the Mental Health Act to afford protection to those whose freedom of movement has to be severely and frequently restricted.

11.7 Therapists

Commissioners have been made aware of the important contribution being made by physiotherapists and also speech, occupational, art and music therapists. There are significant gaps in the lives of many patients where these services are not provided or are under-resourced. The Commission encourages both purchasers and providers to recognise the immediate and long-term benefits of these therapies.

12.
LEGAL MATTERS

12.1   Trusts Managers and Non-Executive Directors

A particular cause for concern throughout the past year has been the continued uncertainty about the extent to which the Boards of NHS Trust Hospitals have been able to delegate their managerial responsibilities under the Mental Health Act to a sub-committee. This opportunity exists in respect of Health Authorities and enabled the appointment of a panel of people with both interest and expertise in mental health matters. The confirmation by the Department of Health that a drafting error in the National Health Service and Community Care Act 1990 prevents this being done by Trusts has placed considerable responsibility on non-executive directors, many of whom have had no previous experience of the duties of Mental Health Act Managers. The consequences for detained patients who have a right of appeal to managers and who look to managers to supervise the operation of the Act were potentially considerable.

The Mental Health Act Commission has given what support it can to Trusts who have found themselves in this position and has co-operated with the National Association of Health Authorities and Trusts (NAHAT) in providing training opportunities to non-executive directors throughout the country. The Commission has also encouraged Ministers to seek early amendment.

12.2   Law Commission Consultation Papers on Mentally Incapacitated Adults and Decision Making

In its Fourth Biennial Report the Mental Health Act Commission referred to the work being done in this area by the Law Commission and reported on the proposals that it had made to the Law Commission. In the intervening period this work has continued and the Law Commission has now published three more papers on this important topic:

i.   Consultation Paper 128:
    Mentally Incapacitated Adults and Decision Making: A New Jurisdiction.

ii. Consultation Paper 129:
    Mentally Incapacitated Adults and Decision Making: Medical Treatment and Research

iii. Consultation Paper 130:
    Mentally Incapacitated Adults and Decision Making: Public Law Protection.

The Mental Health Act Commission has met with the Law Commission and has responded in writing to these papers, generally welcoming their content. Although the proposals have not attracted universal support in every detail the Mental Health Act Commission is in no doubt that they represent the best attempt so far to place this difficult area within a constructive legal and ethical framework. Legislative action will be needed, and although the proposals do not impinge directly on compulsory admission within the Mental Health Act it may

be appropriate to examine these issues together in the course of any future review of mental health legislation (See Chapter 17).

12.3   Children and Mental Health

The past two years have seen some uncertainty introduced into the medical treatment of children and young persons. It has been assumed that the ruling in *Gillick* allowed a degree of autonomy to minors who had the capacity to decide whether they required treatment or not. Treatment against the will of a minor who had such capacity could not take place save within the safeguards of the Mental Health Act. At a procedural level the requirements of the Children Act 1990 have introduced doubt into the minds of many professionals as to whether they should proceed within the Children Act or the Mental Health Act. At a substantive level, two cases, *Re R (A Minor) (Wardship Consent to Treatment) and Re W (A Minor)* have eroded the proposition set out above by deciding that although a minor may have the right to consent to treatment, he or she does not have the right of veto over treatment and thus a parent or local authority having wardship may consent on their behalf, although the wishes and the age of the minor are important considerations to be taken into account.

The Mental Health Act Commission intends, in collaboration with others to address this issue in the near future.

12.4   Effect of Delay in Court Hearing on Setting Aside Nearest Relatives

The Mental Health Act Commission has had cause for concern where, following an application to set aside the nearest relative by means of the provision in Section 29 of the Mental Health Act, delay has occurred in setting down the case for hearing. The effect of such an application is to extend the period of operation of Section 2 beyond 28 days until the application to the court is dealt with. However, there is no provision in the Act for a Mental Health Review Tribunal to hear an appeal in these circumstances. The effect of delay, therefore, is to maintain the patients' detention but to deprive them of a right to independent review.

Following correspondence with the Lord Chancellor's Department, the Commission has received assurances that if the procedure is correctly used then there should be no undue delay.

12.5   Proposals for Community Supervision and Supervised Leave

The Mental Health Act Commission has been closely involved in the discussions which followed the proposals of the Royal College of Psychiatrists for a Community Supervision Order (1993) and the setting up of Department of Health working party of officials to examine the legal powers on the care of people in the community. In both written and oral evidence to the Health Committee of the House of Commons (1993) and the Departmental Review Team the Commission was unable to support the proposal of the Royal College in the form in which it was put and made counter proposals. The Commission felt that the powers of compulsory admission in the Mental Health Act went further than was sometimes appreciated that there was scope in the Act for the greater use of guardianship and that changes in the law should be made in the context of a more wide ranging review of the legislation (See Chapter 17). The Commission felt able to support the proposal that legislative change could be made so that patients detained under Section 3 or Section 37 and who were in their third continuous period of detention could be granted leave of absence for more than the 6 months currently authorised.

12.6   The Witham Case

Reference was made in the Fourth Biennial Report (para 11.1) to this case which involved the proposed administration of a drug, Goserelin (trade name Zoladex) to a patient for the purposes of reducing sexual drive. In July 1991 Mr Witham's claim for negligence against the Commission was struck out, but he was granted leave to appeal. The matter was concluded when Mr Witham subsequently withdrew his appeal. The case highlights and clarifies a number of important aspects of the Commission's procedures for operating both Section 57 and 58 of the Act and these were referred to in the Fourth Biennial Report.

12.7   Mental Health Act Cases

A number of important cases have clarified points of law under the Mental Health Act in the period covered by this report.

R v De Souza

The Commission welcomed the outcome of this case which clarified the powers of police officers to enter private premises in order to return an absconding patient to hospital.

R v Cannon Park Mental Health Review Tribunal, ex parte A

This case has significant implications, deciding as it does that where a patient with psychopathic disorder is found by a Mental Health Review Tribunal to be untreatable within the terms of the Act then it must discharge them. The Commission understands that this case is the subject of an appeal.

R v Managers of South Western Hospital, ex parte M

This case usefully examined the inter-relationship between the decision of a Mental Health Review Tribunal and the powers of doctors and social workers to re-admit the patient following discharge from a Section. The patient was discharged by the tribunal from her Section 2 on 14th December 1992 (with effect from 17th) on the basis that although the patient was suffering from mental disorder it was not of a nature or degree which warranted her detention in hospital for assessment. However, the responsible medical officer none the less recommended on the same day, that she be admitted under Section 3 for treatment, and an application to the hospital managers was made to this effect by an approved social worker.

It was argued on the patient's behalf that, once a tribunal had decided to discharge, the decision should be respected to the extent that it cannot be nullified by an application to detain which follows closely on the tribunal's discharge where there is no change of circumstances. Such a detention frustrates the tribunal decision and, it was argued, could justify a writ of *habeas corpus*.

The Court rejected this argument and held that there was an absolute right to make such an application irrespective of the tribunal's decision to discharge. It was held that the managers have an obligation to consider such an application on its merits and whilst this included an obligation to take into account the fact that the tribunal had recently discharged the patient there is nothing in the Act to indicate that a recent tribunal decision was capable of fettering their discretion.

R v Ealing District Health Authority ex parte Fox

This important case made clear that the duty referred to in Section 117 of the Mental Health Act is a real one, applicable in individual cases.

Following the direction of a Mental Health Review Tribunal that the patient should be conditionally discharged, pending satisfactory arrangements for aftercare, the Health Authority found that it was unable to provide such care, as the Authority's doctors opposed the scheme and refused to provide the necessary supervision. The patient remained in hospital.

In an action for judicial review it was held that the Health Authority had not discharged its statutory obligations by merely accepting its own doctor's opinions. It had a duty to make arrangements with other Health Authorities, or if it failed, it ought to refer the matter back to the Secretary of State.

12.8   Mental Health Act 1983

Reference is made in Chapter 17 to aspects of the current Act which in the Commission's view require urgent review. Chapter 17 also clarifies why the Commission feels that a review of the whole Act is necessary.

REFERENCES

Royal College of Psychiatrists (1993) Community Supervision Orders — Royal College of Psychiatrists

Health Committee of the House of Commons (1993), Legal Powers on the care of mentally ill people in the Community — HMSO. 1993

13.
RACE AND CULTURE

13.1 Introduction

The Commission views with concern the disadvantages that continue to be experienced by people from black and minority ethnic communities who come into contact with the mental health services. A discussion paper issued by the Department of Health and Home Office (1992) lists findings relating mainly to the apparent over-diagnosis of schizophrenia among African-Caribbeans, the over-representation of black people among those being detained under the Mental Health Act and evidence that black patients are given relatively high doses of medication compared to white people. All these matters have been noted in successive Biennial Reports of the Commission. The Department of Health/Home Office paper, a recent publication from MIND (1993) and the comments in the Report of the Inquiry into the death of Orville Blackwood at Broadmoor Hospital (SHSA, 1993) taken together suggest strongly that such fundamental problems need to be addressed urgently and comprehensively before, or at the same time, specifically "cultural" matters are considered, such as the provision of interpreters or a choice of food.

As the Orville Blackwood report points out, a "colour-blind" approach to patients inevitably ignores the experience of racism suffered by black people in British society. That report highlights very dramatically the serious consequences arising from the failure by mental health services to adequately recognise the fact that psychiatry tends to reflect "white, middle class and eurocentric" values which can act as real barriers to the provision of relevant and effective care and treatment. Whilst the resolution of these problems may well require fundamental change, significant advances may be achieved by strategies such as:

a. Instituting effective equal opportunities policies.

b. Establishing valid systems of ethnic monitoring and incorporating these into planning and development.

c. Regulating the use of potentially destructive forms of control and treatment.

d. Increasing the sensitivity of professional staff to the extent to which institutional racism affects professional practices through training and education.

13.2 Equal Opportunities Policies

In its Third Biennial Report, the Commission called on each Health Authority to institute an effective equal opportunities policy (EOP) in employment. Although such policies are now common place, they are usually far from effective in the authorities visited by the Commission. The report of the inquiry into the death of Orville Blackwood points to the lack of senior managers from ethnic communities either at Broadmoor or at the Special Health Services Authorities (SHSA). The Commission sees this as a more general problem that hospitals, Trusts and Health Authorities need to face up to by employing pro-active strategies. Clearly, equal opportunities in employment are related to providing equitable services, "sectioning" procedures, and treat-

ment. However, the Commission considers that each mental health service should develop an EOP for service provision as a separate package from its EOP for employment of staff addressing issues of equality of access to services, including psychotherapy and counselling. There is a persistent impression among most client groups that psychotherapy is seldom offered to black people and perhaps to people from minority ethnic groups in general.

13.3 Ethnic Monitoring

Although it is the policy of the Department of Health that ethnic monitoring of all health services should be in place by April 1994, few hospitals and Health Authorities seem to be preparing for this. In many places, little thought has been given to the implications of monitoring and in many instances no training in ethnic monitoring has been provided for staff. In the view of the Commission, ethnic monitoring should not be undertaken lightly. Both staff and patients participating in a monitoring process must be clear about the need for, and purpose of, monitoring. The Commission strongly recommends that the Department of Health should issue specific and detailed guidelines on the procedures to be followed during ethnic monitoring and the staff training for its implementation.

Furthermore, monitoring is not an end in itself. It must be linked into planning development, education and training. One approach is for management to define a race equality policy (similar perhaps to the Commission's own policy given in Appendix 15) and then use monitoring systems to formulate strategies for action linked to forward planning. (Fernando, 1993). A failure to have in place a clear means of using the results of monitoring for service improvement may result in monitoring being seen as a waste of time and, even worse, exacerbating racist stereotyping leading to a worsening of the quality of the service for minority ethnic communities.

13.4 Regulation of Methods of Control

The Code of Practice indicates that physical restraint, seclusion and the use of medication in some circumstances are not forms of treatment. The Commission has seen clear evidence supporting the general impression that seclusion is used more frequently in the case of African-Caribbean patients, compared to white people. The Commission's Third and Fourth Biennial Reports raised concerns about the use of high levels of medication for African-Caribbean patients. The effects of racism on the use of medication and seclusion within the psychiatric system has been raised by the report of the inquiry into the death of Orville Blackwood. Therefore, it is imperative that each mental health service develops a system through which professionals responsible for instituting control are accountable for their decisions to management through (for example) post-incident enquiries with advocacy for patients.

The Commission understands that the Commission for Racial Equality (CRE) has abandoned its proposed investigation into treatment of psychiatric patients. The results of such an investigation may have provided a basis for instituting ways of regulating the use of medication in the control of patients. The Commission hopes the Department of Health may wish to collaborate with the CRE in instituting an investigation into the use of medication within the psychiatric system which addresses the issue of racism.

13.5   Education in Issues of Race and Culture

The report of inquiry into the death of Orville Blackwood draws attention to the ease with which psychiatrists may "slip into the use of stereotypes" in both diagnosis and the assessment of "dangerousness". There is a growing literature on the effects of racism on psychiatric practice (see Fernando 1991). The reference quoted in the Department of Health/Home Office paper indicate that the over-diagnosis of "schizophrenia" among African-Caribbean people in Britain is now well established. Other publications (eg: Webb-Johnson, 1991; MIND, 1993) have questioned the usefulness of some aspects of the present psychiatric system in a multi-ethnic society. Education and training need to address all these issues.

The Commission welcomes efforts to improve social work training through, for example, Paper 30(CCETSW, 1991) and Paper 19.26 (CCETSW, 1993) published by the Central Council for Education and Training of social workers and would like to see other bodies concerned with professional education following this example. However, since the education of most professional groups in the mental health field, especially psychiatrists and nurses, do not seem to address these issues adequately, it is important that service providers institute their own in-service training in race and culture for professional staff of all disciplines. In our view, such training should cover at least racism awareness, anti-racist practice and theoretical knowledge about concepts of illness held in non-Western cultures. The training should be supported and attended by staff at all levels, led by senior managers. The report of inquiry into the death of Orville Blackwood pointed out (on page 54) that by failing to attend fully a course on race awareness, senior managers at Broadmoor Hospital sent a "message" to staff that was "unmistakable".

References to other issues that have concerned the Commission with regard to mental health services for people from black and ethnic minority communities can be found at Chapters 3, 10 and 18.

REFERENCES

CCETSW (1991) *Paper 30, DipSW. Rules and Requirements for the Diploma in Social Work. Second Edition.* Central Council for Education and Training in Social Work, London.

CCETSW (1993) *Paper 19.26. Approved Social Worker and Mental Health Officer Training. Guidelines for Developing Antiracist Practice.* Central Council for Education and Training in Social Work, London.

Department of Health and Home Office (1992) *Services for People from Black and Ethnic Minority Groups. Issues of Race and Culture. A Discussion Paper.*

Fernando, S (1991) *Mental Health, Race and Culture,* Macmillan/MIND, London

Fernando, S. (1993) Racism and Xenophobia. *Innovation, 6, 1, 9–19*

MIND (1993) *MIND's Policy on Black and Minority Ethnic People and Mental Health, Policy Paper 1.* MIND, London

Special Hospital Services Authority, 1993. *Report of the Committee of Inquiry into the Death in Broadmoor Hospital of Orville Blackwood and a Review of the Death of Two Other Afro-Caribbean Patients* SHSA, London 1993

Webb-Johnson 1991

14.
CARE IN THE COMMUNITY

14.1 NHS and Community Care Act 1990

(a) Introduction

The last two years have been dominated by the implementation of the complex provisions of the National Health Services and Community Care Act 1990. This resulted in delays in some areas in implementation of the Care Programme Approach and Section 117 aftercare procedures, whilst social services and health authorities gradually worked through the difficulties of the new system. In some localities the simultaneous introduction of NHS Trusts has created complexities for joint planning and joint working. The role of the Community Care Support Force appears to have been of positive benefit, but its guidance in relation to the special needs of mentally disordered people was late in arriving.

Prior to meetings with Social Services Departments the Commission now asks to see the documentation of local care procedures. In the case of Community Care, it has to be said that some very complex, contract-bound documents for assessment, planning and review have resulted in often major and at times idiosyncratic differences between neighbouring social services departments. Understanding these arcane variations can present real problems for local health service workers who cover a number of social services authorities, as well as observers from the Commission.

Most authorities have incorporated statutory after-care requirements in Care Planning arrangements, but there are still some worrying gaps, particularly in urban areas. (see paragraph 14.2) These tend to be localities in which dissatisfaction has been expressed about disparities in the allocation of Transitional Grant funding. Operational staff in these local community mental health services, both health and social services, are concerned that the combination of gaps in joint procedures together with scarcity of financial resources does not augur well for their clients.

The Commission has had some direct discussion with the Association of Directors of Social Services over the last two years in order to identify the consequences of the new structures and statutory duties now placed on Health and Social Services by the Act. These will form an important item for the next Biennial Report review period.

(b) The National Health Service re-organisation

The last two years has seen the rapid development of the separation of the roles of the purchaser and provider in the Health Service with the establishment of a considerable number of NHS Trusts. At times it has proved difficult for the Commission as a national body to maintain familiarity with the numerous changes in each Commission Visiting Team (CVT) area, as new NHS Trusts have come into being. Recently the amalgamation of purchasers in consortia have started to change the nature of the planning interface and lines of accountability. There have also been additional local concerns about the emergency role of GP fund-holders in setting the pattern of future services. Some GP fund-holders, or consortia, are opting to appoint their own counsellors and Community Psychiatric Nurses (CPNs), which many Trusts fear may undermine the viability of their own Community Mental Health Teams (CMHTs). In addition if local Social Services resources also come under pressure, it is feared that the role of Social Workers in relation to CMHTs may become more marginalised.

Commissioners have welcomed the increased presence of user groups and advocacy schemes relating to community services. These are much needed as pressure groups in the present climate of change and restructuring in both the health and social services in order to ensure that the service users perspective is taken fully into account.

(c) Definition of NHS services

Commissioners have noticed discrepancies in the way in which Health Authorities are defining their duties to provide care and accommodation for mentally disordered people. In some districts, small local units are provided as part of the NHS. In other districts such accommodation is left to social services, voluntary or private sector initiatives in which the residents contribute to the cost on a means tested basis in comparison with NHS accommodation which is free at the point of delivery. A result of this disparity is that in some districts, NHS beds are blocked because of the reluctance of patients or their relatives to accept transfer to non-NHS accommodation.

14.2 Section 117 of the Mental Health Act. Aftercare

Since the Commission's last Report Social Service Departments, Health Authorities, and Trusts have been introducing the Care Programme Approach and have incorporated Section 117 paperwork into the care programme documentation. The Commission reminds Social Services Departments and Health Authorities of the legal obligations imposed by Section 117 and the consequent importance of ensuring that the relevant documentation is easily retrievable by professionals involved in the care of patients and is available for monitoring by Commissioners. The Commission welcomes the work done in relation to the Care Programme Approach, but stresses that the new system should not have the effect of diluting the implementation of Section 117.

The recording of unmet needs by personnel who are arranging or negotiating the provision of aftercare remains very patchy. The Commission emphasises the importance of recording and collecting this information for the purposes of planning a service, the shape of which within the overall limits of available resources is primarily determined by the needs of its customers.

The case of R v Ealing District Health Authority ex parte Fox made it clear that the duty referred to in Section 117 of the Mental Health Act is a real one, applicable in individual cases — see Chapter 12.

Problems identified by Commissioners about the implementation of Section 117 include:

a. Inadequate recording of the Section 117 aftercare plans under this section in any recognised format, frequently with no record of unmet needs.

b. A tendency in some hospitals for individual patient Section 117 meetings to be held at the last moment prior to the patients discharge. In a few instances Commissioners have found such meetings taking place after the patients discharge.

c. A laxity in some areas in the use of the Section 117 register and the failure to make effective use of flagging systems to hold meetings for the purpose of reviewing the needs of the patient, if any, for continuing aftercare. Equally important is the opportunity such meetings provide to consider the adequacy and effectiveness of the aftercare being provided at the time of the review.

d. The practice of some responsible medical officers in sending patients on leave of absence without a Section 117 after-care programme in place. The Commission draws attention to the provisions of paragraph 20.4(a)(i) of the revised Code of Practice.

e. Section 117 planning meetings not infrequently do not include family, formal or informal carers or the patient. In addition they often exclude staff from day units and voluntary services who will be providing part of the patients aftercare.

The Commission would strongly remind purchasers that they have a statutory obligation to ensure that their providers are meeting the requirements of Section 117.

Over the last two years the Commission has observed a noticeable increase in the number of community based mental health services responding sensitively to the needs of minority ethnic communities. Such services have often been initiated and developed by the voluntary sector.

In many areas, however, the Commission has noted an insufficient range of services available in the community to meet all the needs of mentally ill people.

14.3   Guardianship

Although some authorities have shown a welcome willingness to use Guardianship more frequently the general tendency is for it to be under-used or even actively discouraged. In their visits to Social Service Departments Commissioners always make reference to Guardianship, but have generally found no interest in increasing its use amongst managers. Approved Social Workers frequently feel deterred by the complexities of the administrative procedures of Social Service Departments even though they acknowledge the value of Guardianship as an alternative to hospital admission. Recent statements by the Association of Directors of Social Services in favour of a more extensive use of guardianship are welcomed, but will require an active programme of promotion.

It would be unfortunate if the discussion and possible implementation of Supervised Discharge Orders (Chapter 19) were to restrict the use of Guardianship to patients who are difficult to manage in the community. The need to provide such statutory support in the community to, in particular, elderly confused people and those with mental impairment or severe mental impairment is emphasised by the impact of the implementation of the National Health Service and Community Care Act.

14.4   Approved Social Workers (ASWs)

Commissioners have been pleased to note the continuing expressions of regard for the competence and qualities of professional judgement of Approved Social Workers (ASWs). Good standards of staff selection, training and appraisal appear to have become more widely established. In its evidence to the House of Commons Health Committee on Community Supervision Orders the Commission recommended that professional audit of the work of ASWs work should now be introduced, as it has been widely for Responsible Medical Officers (RMOs).

There has been very encouraging evidence of the concern of ASWs for Code of Practice standards, and a lively interest in the amendments to be included in the revised Code of Practice (see Chapter 9).

(a)   Gaps in service provision

There continue to be gaps in out of office hours cover, particularly in those areas which rely on an adjoining authority's emergency duty team. The Commission has had to express concerns that liaison between day and night staff is ill-served by such agency arrangements, and that ASWs providing such a service may find it difficult, if not impossible, to assess accurately the alternatives to admission under the Act in localities with which they are unfamiliar. The Commission has also been given examples where patients have been put at risk through unacceptable delays in providing out of hours ASW assessments. It has also been reported to Commissioners that child care work which is referred to such out of hours services usually takes priority over mental health referrals.

The number of ASWs required to provide adequate cover is a controversial subject. Ten years into the legislation, no guidelines have been issued as to how many ASWs a Social Services Department should approve and appoint taking into account differences in geographical area, the needs of various types of population and their density. ASWs have frequently reported to the Commission a reduction in their numbers at a time when there is a clear increased use of the Act, especially in urban areas.

(b)   Training of ASWs

Refresher training continues to be sparsely offered, if at all. However, in more recent months, the Commission has learned of neighbouring departments uniting to offer a programme of such training as is offered; such training has been seen to be valuable and has been well received by ASWs. Some Social Service Departments rely on their own departmental ASW meetings to augment their own refresher training. Whilst the Commission applauds such involvement, it regards this practice as unacceptable if the Authority itself does not take overall responsibility for providing such training as part of its staff training and development strategy. Not doing so fails to acknowledge the critical need for continuing training for staff involved in the implementation of the Mental Health Act.

Circulars 51/86 Wales and LAC (86)15 England state that Local Authorities should give approval only to those social workers who are shown to have the relevant experience and competence.

CCETSW paper 19.19 (revised edition) 1983 "Requirements and Guidance for the training of social workers to be considered for approval under the Mental Health Act", has taken this further, and makes it a requirement that "competence" should be assessed as part of any ASW training programme. The Commission welcomes these extended provisions.

(c) Role of ASWs

At a number of local meetings with Social Service Departments ASWs have said that their role does not comfortably straddle the purchaser/provider split introduced into Social Service Departments following the implementation of the National Health Service and Community Care Act 1990. ASWs carrying out duties within the meaning of the 1983 Mental Health Act are generally located on the "purchaser" side of the split and they are primarily involved in assessment work. Constraints on providers not infrequently appear to result in ASWs no longer being able to use community facilities as an alternative to admission.

14.5 Community Support Teams

The Commission is pleased to note the excellent multidisciplinary work undertaken by many community support teams set up as joint ventures by Health Authorities and social Service Departments. Many have been established with revenue made available from the Mental Illness Specific Grant. In such schemes, 70 per cent of the money becomes available from Central Government with the balance provided by local authorities. Concern is often expressed over the time limit for funding of such schemes.

14.6 Mental Nursing Homes

(a) The legislation

Whilst the NHS and Community Care Act 1990 has not affected the legislation governing mental nursing homes it has added some impetus to the growth in this sector of care noted in the Commission's previous reports. The number and variety of mental nursing homes continue to increase. These include some enterprising partnerships between the NHS and private or voluntary organisations working in the field of mental health. Such experiments can sometimes offer new and refreshing approaches in the provision of care. However they do not always sit easily with the governing legislation which was framed when there was a clear distinction between the responsibilities of social service and health authorities, and when most institutional provision was in large mental hospitals.

The Registered Homes Act 1984 continues to require District Health Authorities to register and inspect nursing homes and social service authorities to do the same for residential care homes. Since April 1993 joint registration and inspection units have been introduced to fulfil these separate but similar duties. However, any establishment providing nursing care not solely vested in or managed by an NHS authority, no matter how constituted, must still be registered as a nursing home. Mental nursing homes must be separately registered and may only detain patients under the Mental Health Act if specifically registered for this purpose under Section 23 of the Registered Homes Act. District Health Authorities may thus find themselves with the invidious responsibility of registering and inspecting nursing homes of which they are joint proprietors. This is not a problem where the health service partner is an NHS Trust.

The nature of any contract between purchasers and a registered nursing home which may include services for detained patients should be carefully considered as it could determine which authority exercises those functions of the statutory managers relating to the review and discharge of patients detained in the home.

It must be hoped that innovative and experimental methods of caring for disordered people in a variety of settings will not be hindered by an increasingly anachronistic legislative framework because the Commission's experience is that the quality of such care is generally of a high order.

(b) Registration

The Fourth Biennial Report (Para 13.6) listed a number of other problems in connection with private mental nursing homes. Most of these still apply. A continuing difficulty for the Commission is to discover which mental nursing homes are registered to accept detained patients and when any such homes are first registered. Registering authorities are not statutorily required to notify the Commission of new registrations and do not always respond to requests for information. Some registration staff appear not to appreciate the requirement for the specific registration of homes authorised to detain patients nor to be able to explain to prospective applicants the procedural consequences of compliance with the Mental Health Act which flow from such registrations.

(c) National Association of Health Authorities and Trusts

In October 1991 the Commission and the National Association of Health Authorities and Trusts (NAHAT) jointly sponsored a conference for District Health Authority registration officers and the staffs of mental nursing homes to promote a greater understanding of the need for and consequences of registering homes to accept detained patients. The event was very well attended and disclosed a great need for more information and training, not only with regard to mental nursing homes, but over the much wider field of nursing home registration in general.

One outcome was a decision to revise and extend the guidance relating to mental nursing homes contained in the Handbook on the Registration and Inspection of Nursing Homes published by NAHAT in 1985. Funding for this was sought from the Department of Health and a decision is still awaited.

While this uncertainty about the existence and classification of nursing homes authorised to accept detained patients continues, there remains the possibility of nursing homes existing which may not be properly registered, of which the Commission is unaware, and where patients may be unlawfully confined in the mistaken belief that the provisions of the Mental Health Act apply.

(d) Residential care provision

Places in the private sector for the care of detained patients have continued to increase. Changes in Social Security funding for independent sector residential care were the original impetus of current changes, and an unanticipated but main contributor to the closure of long stay hospital provision. The access by monitoring agencies to residential homes has remained equivocal — a situation which the Commission finds unacceptable in relation to patients placed in such homes on Section 17 leave.

The welfare of these patients may need special safeguards if, as present trends suggest, the over provision of residential homes and greater emphasis on alternative care in the home makes their commercial viability uncertain. Health workers are voicing uncertainties in the face of the setting by Social Services of greatly changed priorities on the availability of residential care in individual packages.

In a number of localities Commissioners have expressed particular concerns regarding the de facto detention of residents in residential and nursing homes. This often relates to highly decentralised and widely distributed services , where the awareness and experience of Code of Practice standards by staff can be inadequate. The Commission will need to monitor each local situation as closely as possible, but at a time when the changes in health and social services themselves can be difficult to follow, the remoter reaches of the independent sector may be very inaccessible.

(e) Care programme approach

It is too early to know with certainty what will be the effect of the Care Programme Approach, introduced from April 1991, in relation to services provided by mental nursing homes. It is already clear that in many areas the statutory responsibility placed on health and social service authorities by Section 117 to provide after care for former detained hospital patients is being subsumed in care programmes. Whilst this development is welcomed it does not relieve the authorities of their statutory duty nor the Commission of the need to monitor the arrangements. The trend to make greater use of mental nursing homes for this purpose noted in the Fourth Report is likely to continue.

15.
DEATHS OF DETAINED PATIENTS

The Commission requests notification of all deaths of detained patients (see letter at Appendix 5) and wherever possible Commissioners attend inquests. Not all deaths are followed by inquests but the majority of unexpected deaths are. A coroner's jury will be called on those occasions where the coroner thinks it is in the public interest. The primary reason for a Commissioner to attend an inquest is to ascertain information which is relevant to the exercise of powers and duties under the Act, insofar as procedures or facilities for detained patients are defective or inadequate. The information gathered may be useful locally in that it may identify problems in a particular unit, or may contribute to the Commission's understanding of more widespread problems. The role of the Commissioners at inquests is primarily as an observer.

Between 1991 and 1993 the Commission was notified of 391 deaths and recorded information on 143 inquests. Deaths which were not followed by an inquest were reported to be of those dying from expected natural causes or physical disorders clearly eastablished at post mortem. Of those reviewed at inquest, 95 (66%) were of sudden unexpected deaths of which 72 (76% of sudden deaths) were a result of self harm and a further 9 (9% of sudden deaths) occurred during a period of servere mental disturbance where the cause of death has been attributed to a number of different factors in which pre-exisitng physical conditions, medication, restraint, physical over activity and mental arousal may have played a significant part but where medication appeared to play an important role.

The Commission is aware that these figures may reflect an under-reporting of deaths by hospitals and is concerned by the apparent frequency of potentially avoidable deaths from deliberate self harm in the course of an admission or during treatment for severe behavioural disturbance. More detailed analysis of the data is now in progress to establish whether these deaths occur more frequently than could reasonably be expected and to identify any trends which might assist providers of mental health care in decreasing the number of untoward incidents and deaths of detained people.

The first area of concern is the frequency with which sudden deaths are not followed by a coroner's inquest. The coroner relies on the report of the Responsible Medical Officer and the report of the pathologist who conducted the post mortem to decide whether or not it is necessary to hold an inquest to establish the cause of death. The Commission is concerned that there may be occasions where prescribed medication may have contributed to sudden death from disease but there has been no opportunity to explore the likelihood of this. It is helpful for both staff and relatives of the deceased to have a full investigation and explanation of events leading to death. The Commission recommends that there should be an inquest held on all sudden and unexpected deaths of detained patients where the deceased was receiving psychotropic medication, even where the post mortem reveals an obvious immediate antecedent event.

Deaths caused by deliberate self harm do not necessarily lead to an inquest verdict of suicide. An open verdict or one of accidental death is recorded where no intent to commit suicide can be established. Deaths from self harm have occurred in the course of treatment of an acute episode of mental illness when staff were either insufficiently aware of the patient's self destructive feelings or alternatively patients were inadequately observed or supervised. Some of these deaths may be preventable. Staff require training in the assessment of risk and in techniques of close observation which are not perceived as burdensome by patients.

The role of psychotropic medication in the sudden deaths of patients is a matter of concern to the Commission. It is hoped that a more searching analysis of the data now held by the Commission will assist in identifying the circumstances when patients are most at risk. A review of the circumstances of eight deaths reported to the Commission between 1990 and 1992 revealed a characteristic pattern of escalating quantities of mixed neuroleptic drugs and other sedatives given intramuscularly every few hours, often prescribed by inexperienced staff with very little supervision. Sudden cardiotoxic collapse during a period of physiological arousal is a well known adverse consequence of neuroleptics, such as chlorpromazine and pimozide, and generally regarded as a rare phenomenon but some deaths may have been due to synergistic or high dosage effects of multiple drugs administered in boluses given too close together.

The Commission recommends that Hospital Managers should instigate an internal hospital inquiry of the circumstances of all sudden deaths of detained patients. Even where a coroner's inquest verdict is that death was from natural causes, there are often lessons to be learned. All unexpected deaths occurring to patients receiving psychotropic medication should be reported to the Committee on Safety of Medicines through the yellow card voluntary reporting system.

The Commission recommends that all psychiatric units should develop treatment protocols to assist doctors treating severely disturbed patients, that "PRN" medication should be limited as to its maximum dosage over a specific period and that wherever possible, senior doctors, preferably consultants, should treat seriously disturbed patients. At present most patients are treated by trainees only. It would also be helpful for experienced senior nurses skilled in restraint and observation techniques to be available for psychiatric emergencies.

At the time of going to press the more detailed analysis of deaths of detained patients in the years covered by this report was not yet available. It is hoped that the full results will be available in early 1994, and reveal whether or not these incidents are relatively infrequent or matters of concern nationwide. Finally, the Commission would like to remind hospitals and mental nursing homes that all deaths of detained patients should be notified to the Commission. The information should include the deceased patient's demographic details, psychiatric diagnosis and cause of death, if known, and whether or not a post mortem and inquest are planned.

16.
THE FUTURE ROLE AND FUNCTION OF THE COMMISSION

16.1 Introduction

In November 1992 the Commission was invited to review its statutory remit, composition and organisation and to submit any resulting proposals to Ministers for their consideration. In undertaking its review the Commission has paid particular attention to the changes in mental health services over the first 10 years of its existence and its own experience of undertaking its statutory responsibility during that period. It has also considered the recommendations of the Committee of Inquiry into Ashworth Hospital (see Chapter 5) and taken account of the recent development of mechanisms for monitoring quality standards locally as a result of the purchaser/provider split consequent upon the NHS and Community Care Act 1990.

The work of the review continued throughout early 1993. Members of the Commission, at a conference in May 1993, gave support to the principles underpinning the proposed changes and the final report, when agreed by the Central Policy Committee, will be submitted to Ministers in due course. There will, no doubt, be widespread consultation with statutory and other agencies concerned before any changes are implemented. The Commission welcomes comments on the recommendations outlined below.

The recommendations are made subject to the following assumptions:

a. That no additional financial resources will be allocated to the Commission.

b. That no major change in the provisions of the Mental Health Act 1983 is likely in the short or medium term.

c. That the Commission's credibility in part is based on its multi-disciplinary composition.

d. That the assumptions above do not preclude recommendations about the Commission's remit which might require additional financial resources.

The overall objectives of the proposed changes are to improve the effectiveness of the Commission and to ensure that such improved effectiveness is achieved in the most efficient manner possible.

16.2 Recommendations

(a) The statutory remit

(i) Overall remit

The Commission's remit is confined currently to detained patients. In 1985 the Commission asked Ministers to consider extending the remit to 'de facto' detained patients and this request is still extant. The Commission has concluded that there is a group of people receiving care and treatment for mental disorder in a range of different settings who are subject to elements of compulsion or substitute decision-making and whose rights are not effectively protected. Commissioners often come across circumstances where such concerns have been difficult to pursue on hospital visits because of the limitations on the Commission's remit. In one sense the Commission has already formally been given the opportunity to go outside its specific remit in that its monitoring of the Code of Practice can involve examination of the implementation of those parts of the Code which relate to all patients.

For these reasons the Commission would propose that the general remit be revised to read:

"The Commission shall keep under review the exercise of powers and the discharge of duties conferred or imposed by the Mental Health Act 1983 (or any other legislation, power or authority relevant to Mental Health), in relation to patients (i.e. persons suffering or appearing to be suffering from mental disorder), with special reference to patients detained or liable to be detained under the Act."

The Commission would recommend that any such direction from the Secretary of State, which the Commission recognises would have to be subjected to prior consultation with any interested bodies, would indicate that the Commission in pursuance of this wider remit would be required to publish, probably on an annual basis, a programme setting out its priority in respect of its varying functions.

(ii) Complaints jurisdiction

The Commission has considered the recommendations of the Ashworth Report that the Commission should cease to investigate complaints. In the light of the recommendations about the Commission's composition and structure referred to below, it has concluded that it would not be right to accept the Ashworth Report's recommendation but, as an alternative, to improve the performance of its complaints function. The current emphasis that Health Authorities, Trusts and Social Services Departments are giving to the handling of complaints should result in fewer complaints coming to the Commission.

In addition, if the Commission were able to ensure that complaints coming to it are referred first to the relevant local complaints procedure, then the Commission's position as ultimate 'long stop' need not be disturbed. At the same time the recommendation of the Ashworth Report that the Secretary of State either at the instigation of the Commission or on her own initiative be empowered to direct the Commission to inquire into any matter which she feels appropriate is supported.

(b) The Commission's powers

In pursuit of its statutory responsibilities, the Commission has only one executive power and that is peripheral: to adjudicate decisions to withhold Special Hospital patients' mail.

The Commission lacks any effective sanction. Where Commissioners identify bad practice and their representations make no impact then, ultimately, recourse can be had to the Secretary of State or to the Biennial Report. There have been however a number of cases where the lack of a sanction has been a problem.

For these reasons the Commission has concluded that consideration should be given to a Commission notification procedure, in the form of a letter to the managers, used very sparingly, where there is a blatant bad practice primarily in relation to breaches of the Act. If there was a failure to comply with the notification letter, this could lead to inclusion in an appendix to the Biennial Report.

(c) The composition and deployment of Commissioners

At present the Commission every year visits approximately 600 hospitals and mental nursing homes, deals with approximately 500 complaints and organises over 4,000 second opinions. For an organisation of its size this is an enormous and varied undertaking. The administration is the more exacting because of the need to service 90 part-time Commissioners, geographically spread throughout the country and acting in local teams.

The changes proposed here are designed to result in:-

a. An increase in the number of detained patients seen by the Commission in any one year.

b. A greater focus of Commission activity, not only on its current remit (or possibly extended remit) but also within its current remit (i.e. on particular issues identified in accordance with the Commission's own agenda).

c. The Commission making better use of the experience of visits and other Commission activities, not only in relation to individual case follow up but also more generally to assist those responsible for policy development and health and social care provision.

The Commission has concluded that all these considerations lead inevitably to a new structure, the outline of which is set out below:

(i) Full-time Commissioners

It is proposed that there should be a Commission Management Board of full-time (or substantial part-time) members drawn from senior professionals reflecting the existing cross section of disciplines within the Commission. The Chief Executive would become a Member of the Commission. The Chairman/Vice Chairman would be part-time as now. The Board would be responsible for all Commission policy, the management of local programmes of activity and the performance of activity against established quality standards.

(ii) Part-time Commissioners

It is recommended that in addition to the full-time Commissioners, the Commission be composed of local panels of part-time Commissioners. Such persons, drawn from the same multi-disciplinary background as Commissioners, would be responsible for visiting detained patients in their locality and other duties as required by the Commission Board.

Whilst the part-time Commissioners should continue to be appointed by the Secretary of State, the Commission recommends that the administration of the appointment process should be taken over by the Commission and that a more rigorous selection system should be introduced to ensure that appointees possess the necessary skills. At the same time, the Commission recommends the introduction of specific contracts of service for part-time Commissioners, initial probationary periods of appointment and fixed term appointments. Part-time Commissioners would be paid on a daily rate and subject to annual review.

The proposals outlined here would require a realignment of administrative staff to support the new structure. It is also hoped that the proposed structure would foster closer working relationships between administrative staff and professionals and would provide a framework for improved opportunities for staff development and involvement in the work of the Commission.

The changes proposed are designed to improve the efficiency and effectiveness of visiting by part-time Commissioners and at the same time to enhance the role of the Commission as the co-ordinator of Commission activity and the framer and executor of Commission policy.

17.
NEW LEGISLATION FOR MENTAL WELFARE

17.1 Introduction

In the Fourth Biennial Report (Chapter 11) the Commission identified a number of deficiencies in the Mental Health Act that had become apparent after 8 years of its operation. In the subsequent 2 years the Commission has seen further examples of the difficulties caused by these deficiencies. In particular, there have been further incidences reported to the Commission where it has been inappropriate for a person to remain as the nearest relative for the purposes of the Act because, for instance, the patient has in the past been sexually abused by the nearest relative. Such a person cannot be removed from their position as nearest relative under the current provisions of the Act.

17.2 Review of the Mental Health Act

In the period under review and particularly since the beginning of 1993 there has been widespread public concern and discussion about the adequacy of the current arrangements for community care for people with acute psychiatric illness and this debate has included an examination of the adequacy of parts of the Mental Health Act itself. (Chapters 12 and 19). In its evidence to both the Department of Health Review of the Legal Powers on the Care of Mentally Ill People in the Community and the House of Commons Health Committee's Inquiry into Community Supervision Orders the Commission argued that a full review of the 1983 Act is now needed.

On 30th September 1993 the Commission submitted to the Secretary of State for Health a Memorandum setting out in full the Commission's reasons for seeking such a review. This can be found at Appendix 16. Copies of the Memorandum together with its Annexes (not included in this report) can be obtained from the Commission.

18.
THE COMMISSION AND RESEARCH

18.1 Introduction

In the Fourth Biennial Report (Chapter 15) the Commission acknowledged the importance of research both in assisting a proper understanding of how the Mental Health Act works, but also improving the provision of care to, and safeguarding the rights of, detained patients.

In carrying out its statutory responsibilities the Commission also acquires a considerable amount of information that could be used as a subject for high quality academic research.

The Commission has no budget to support research projects or the resources to manage them. The Commission's Research and Information National Standing Committee has continued to oversee the Commission's involvement in research by :

a. Vetting approaches made to the Commission by researchers seeking approval for research proposals.

b. Allowing researchers to use Commission data where this is practical; in this role it acts as the Commission equivalent of a local Research Ethics Committee.

c. Identifying issues relevant to the Commission's statutory remit which it considers would benefit from research.

18.2 Projects in which the Commission has had some Involvement

(a) Commission and Codes — a Study in Law and Public Administration

The Commission was pleased to provide information to and to comment on the paper prepared by, Mr Michael Cavadino of Sheffield University Law Department on the history of the Mental Health Act Commission, and the production of the Code of Practice. An article was published in 'Public Law Magazine' 1993 summer issue entitled "Commission and Codes — A Study in Law and Public Administration".

(b) Increase in the Use of the Mental Health Act in London

The Commission previously reported that funding had been made available for research into the apparent increase in the use of Sections of the Mental Health Act in London.

This research has now been undertaken and completed by Professor Philip Bean and Teresa Nemitz of Loughborough University (Chapter 7). The results of the research showed that the quality of the statistical data about the use of the Mental Health Act collected by the Health Service was so poor that it made research on compulsory admissions almost impossible. There were large discrepancies in the statistical information recorded at various levels in the hierarchy in that, for example, the data published centrally by the Department of Health seemed to bear little or no relation to that produced locally in hospitals.

Several explanations for the discrepancies were identified. The researchers concluded in a report to the Kings Fund, which funded the research, that the value of such statistics for Government planning must be questioned. Whilst the Commission recognises that the research was limited to London and surrounding areas it shares this concern. The researchers recommended that an alternative and more efficient centralised system of collecting and collating such data should be introduced as a matter of priority, and that this be undertaken by the Mental Health Act Commission.

The Commission welcomes this proposal and hopes that the Department of Health will be able to allocate resources for the Commission to be able to fulfil this task. It does so, not specifically to improve the quality of Mental Health Act Statistics but because it has long felt that the rights of detained patients would be protected more effectively if the Commission, like its sister Commissions in Scotland and Northern Ireland was notified of all statutorily significant events that occur while a patient is detained. In this way the Commission could have immediate access to all statutory documentation which would be centrally checked for correctness and accuracy. At the moment the Commission reviews documentation on its statutory visits, but by this time the patient may have been detained for some considerable time or already been discharged from hospital. Modern data systems would enable such information to be extensively and usefully analysed in relation both to individual patients and general trends.

One subsidiary consequence of receiving such information would be that the Commission would almost certainly be able to produce national statistics about the use of the Mental Health Act in England and Wales which are more accurate than those currently published by the Department of Health appear to be. Notwithstanding, the Commission feels that the primary responsibility for such statistics must rest with the Department of Health and not the Commission.

(c) Treatment without consent under Part IV of the Mental Health Act 1983

Both the Third and Fourth Biennial Reports identified the need for a detailed evaluation of the safeguards provided by Section 58 of the Act. Such research has now been undertaken by Philip Fennell (Chapter 7) of the Cardiff Law School and a former member of the Commission. It was funded by the Nuffield Foundation and the full results will be included in "Treatment without Consent; Law Ethics and the Treatment of Mentally Disordered People since 1840" to be published by Routledge in 1994.

The aims of the research were to answer questions about some of the characteristics of the doctors and the patients involved in the Section 58 procedure, about the operation of the emergency treatment and second opinion provisions and about the efficacy of achieving a fair balance between autonomy, beneficence and the protection of others.

The records of one thousand and nine cases held centrally by the Commission between November 1991 and

August 1992 where appointed doctors had authorised psychiatric treatment without consent under Section 58 were analysed. In addition 232 progress reports submitted by responsible medical officers (RMOs) under Section 61 of the Act were also analysed.

The results support the impression that there is a very high agreement rate between RMOs and second opinion doctors appointed by the Commission. It is interesting to note however, that the seven significant changes in treatment plans identified by the research were truly significant and had obviously been the result of considerable discussion between the RMO and the appointed doctor.

The research highlights a wide range of issues including the following:

a. A high proportion of second opinions are provided by a small number of appointed doctors. The Commission is aware of this and has taken administrative steps to ensure a more even spread. (see Chapter 7).

b. Information about ethnicity was incomplete because in 98 cases second opinion doctors did not give this information.

    In this sample, in which approximately ⅓ of the total number of reports received by the commission were scrutinised black patients in general and Black-Caribbean patients in particular were over-represented in relation to the number of black people in the population generally. A much smaller percentage of Black-Caribbean patients received ECT compared to White, Indian, Pakistani and Bangladeshi patients (16% opposed to 55.6%). Most of the Black-Caribbean patients had a diagnosis of schizophrenia, which is treated with anti-psychotic medication, and this may account for the difference.

c. The vast majority (722) of patients were refusing treatment rather than "non volitional" (278). Of those refusing treatment, 308 were regarded as being capable and 414 incapable of understanding the nature, purpose and likely effects of the treatment.

d. A high level of the use of Section 62 was noted. The Code of Practice is quite clear that Section 62 should be used only in a genuine emergency, and the findings suggest that more effective monitoring is indicated. It has been suggested that where treatment under Section 62 has been given, the Commission should require the second opinion doctor to forward a copy of the managers form recording emergency treatment with their report on the visit to the Commission.

e. It was clear that in many instances the second professional (and sometimes even the "nurse"), were drafted in to "get to know" the patient shortly before the second opinion visit simply to comply with the requirement of the Act.

    Even when the professionals did know the patient, second opinion doctors reported that the more junior amongst them felt that they were not qualified to express a view about medical treatment.

f. There was a considerable amount of prescribing over British National Formulary (BNF) recommended doses, and polypharmacy, and there were examples where the appointed doctor was a restraining factor.

Fennell suggests that if a patient is to be given drugs either singly or in combination, which exceed the BNF recommended dose levels, a second opinion should be required, even though the 3 month period where neither the patient's consent or a second opinion is required has not yet expired. He also suggests that there should be a Section 58 type second opinion for medicines for mental disorder where it is proposed to give an informal patient drug doses which singly or in aggregate, exceed BNF dose levels.

The problems associated with polypharmacy are currently being debated by the Commission.

g. Women appear to be more likely to be given second opinion for ECT and black patients appear to be over represented in the group of patients receiving medication doses above BNF limits. The reasons for these findings would require further research.

Fennell stresses the importance of the information held centrally by the Commission, in showing for example how many patients are receiving high dose medication, and whether ethnic minorities are over-represented in certain treatment categories. He emphasises the need for these data to be systematically analyzed.

(d) Commission for Racial Equality

A joint research project with the Commission for Racial Equality (CRE) into procedures used to admit patients under Part II of the Mental Health Act began in April 1991 and was completed in March 1993. The report "An Element of Compulsion" is currently being drafted and will be published shortly. The Commission was disappointed to hear that the investigation into treatment given to psychiatric patients planned by the CRE and supported by the Commission has now been abandoned. The Commission hopes to discuss with the CRE other ways in which the CRE might examine possible discriminatory effects in the provision of psychiatric treatment.

REFERENCES

Cavadino M, 1993, Commission and Codes — A Study in Law and Public Administration — Public Law, Summer 1993.

Bean P. (1993) The Nature and Extent of Compulsory admissions to Mental Hospitals within the four London Regional Health Authorities — Report to the Kings Fund.

Fennell P. (1993), Treatment Without Consent: The operation of The Second — Report to the Nuffield Foundation.

19.
CONTACT AND COLLABORATION WITH OTHER AGENCIES

In the Fourth Biennial Report the Commission highlighted the need for effective contact between the Commission and other agencies which have responsibility for the provision of, or have a specific interest in, the delivery of Mental Health Care Services. The increasing liaison with other organisations which commenced in the period 1989-91 has continued.

19.1   Audit Commission

One of the most significant joint projects in terms not only of interaction but in improving the quality of service provided by the Commission in the future, has been the work being undertaken with the Audit Commission in developing performance indicators in relation to Commission visits.

The aim of the project was to identify suitable indicators that could be developed into measures of performance. A list of recommendations for future action has been produced, some of these the Commission has already actioned and target dates have been set for the implementation of others. This productive joint enterprise is to be continued.

19.2   National Association of Health Authorities and Trusts (NAHAT)

The details and outcome of a very effective joint Commission/NAHAT conference are recorded in the section on Registered Mental Nursing Homes in Chapter 14.

19.3   National Health Service Management Executive (NHSME)

The Commission recognises the need for closer links with the NHSME, and to this end it has been proposed that there should be an annual meeting to discuss items of mutual concern. This should hopefully promote a good understanding of each others problems, and provide a suitable format for promoting joint solutions to issues which have arisen. It is also anticipated that there will be more frequent 'ad hoc' contact with the Performance Management Directorate of the ME to discuss items requiring immediate action.

19.4   House of Commons Health Committee

The Commission gave written and oral evidence to the Committee's Inquiry into Community Supervision Orders which appears to have been influential in determining its conclusions.

Whilst a range of views was expressed amongst Commissioners about the possible extension of legal powers under the Mental Health Act into the Community, they are united in their desire to see an early review of the Mental Health Act (see Chapters 12 and 17).

19.5   Scottish Mental Welfare Commission

The Commission was pleased to have arranged for all administrative staff of the Scottish Mental Welfare Commission to visit the Commission's Nottingham Office. This proved to be an enjoyable and productive exchange of views and information on our respective legislation and procedures.

The Commission has also been able to offer the benefit of its previous experience of Section 57 (psychosurgery) procedures to members of the Scottish Mental Welfare Commission which it is hoped will assist them with the implementation of similar procedures in Scotland.

The Commission has continued to send representatives to both the Scottish and Northern Ireland Commission Conferences. They have also sent members to attend and participate actively in the English and Welsh Commission Conferences as did representatives from the Department of Health in the Republic of Ireland.

19.6 Mental Health Review Tribunals (MHRTs)

In its 1991/1992 Annual Report (London:HMSO) the Council of Tribunals again expressed its grave concern at the continuing problems of delays at MHRTs and their affect in particular on detained patients. Whilst the Commission, as a matter of policy, does not become involved directly in matters concerning the tribunals, it maintains a general interest in their work and there is useful contact with the tribunal offices. Commissioners paid an informal visit to the Liverpool Office of the Tribunal during the period under review in order to discuss problems bought to their attention on visits.

Whilst the Commission is aware of an increase both in tribunal resources and administrative staff over the past 2 years it shares the grave concern of the Council of Tribunals about delays. The Commission acknowledges that there has been improvement in some areas, but it remains its overall impression that the general position about delays remains unchanged. Unlike almost every other type of tribunal, Mental Health Review Tribunals take decisions that directly affect the liberty of the subject and it is the Commission's view that the current position is simply unacceptable. It urges the Secretary of State to take whatever action is necessary to rapidly improve the situation.

19.7   Commission for Racial Equality

(see Chapter 18)

19.8   Training and Public Speaking

Both the Commissioners and Chief Executive have continued to undertake numerous public speaking engagements and have regularly participated in training sessions on Mental Health topics with a wide variety of organisations. This has included visits to America by the Chairman, and to Dublin and Belgium by the Chief Executive.

19.9 Office Placement

The Commission has been able to offer a small number of short term placements to a variety of Mental Health professionals, students and foreign visitors and one that was longer term. In terms of exchanges of ideas and information these have proved to be useful for everybody involved. Requests for placements are considered on an individual basis, and acceptance is dependent on the availability of the limited resources within the Commission.

19.10 Law Society, Institute of Psychiatry and Mental Health Act Commission

The Commission has collaborated with the Law Society and the Institute of Psychiatry in organising a major multi-disciplinary conference to be held in November 1993. The conference will mark the 10th Anniversary of the 1983 Act and it is hoped that it will begin a debate about the shape and form of future mental health legislation. (Chapter 17).

19.11 Association of Directors of Social Services (ADSS)

The Commission has had meetings with the ADSS to discuss matters concerning the role of Social Service Departments and approved social workers under the Mental Health Act.

19.12 Inquiries

In the past 2 years, the Commission has received a number of requests to nominate Commissioners to sit in their personal capacity as members of various Health Service Inquiries. Where such nominations are not potentially prejudicial to any possible future Commission activity, the Commission is happy to respond positively to such requests.

APPENDIX 1

COMMISSION MEMBERS JULY 1991 — JUNE 1993

Ms Anne Aiyegbusi
Mr John Allam
Dr Barry Ashcroft
Mr Allen Ball
Dr Marian Barnes
Mrs Vivien Bellau
Mrs Carolyn Bennett
Mr Reginald Bevan
Sir Louis Blom-Cooper
Dr Tony Blowers
Dr Dorothy Black
Mr John Bowyer (Decd)
Mrs Sarah Breach
Dr Anne Broadhurst
Mr Peter Brotherhood
Mr Martin Brown
Mr Gary Bye
Mr Eric Chitty
Ms Penny Cushing
Mr Alan Dabbs
Dr Ken Day
Mrs Joan Deeley
Prof. Bridget Dimond
Dr Robert Dolan
Dr Desmond Dunleavy
Mrs Phillida Entwistle
Mr Anselm Eldergill
Dr Suman Fernando
Mr John Finch
Mrs Jane Forman-Hardy
Mrs Ros Fraser
Dr Sammy Gaspar
Dr Hema Ghadiali
Dr Neville Gittleson

Dr Edward Gordon
Mr Monty Graham
Prof. Michael Gunn
Miss Margaret Halliday
Dr Max Harper
Dr Agnes Hauck
Canon Arthur Hawes
Dr Pearl Hettiaratchy
Dr David Hide
Mr Gordon Lakes
Mrs Soo Lee
Mr Richard Lingham
Miss Georgina Linton
Mrs Vicki Lipscomb
Mrs Carys Llewelyn-Jones
Dr Tim Malcolm
Mr Steve Manikon
Mrs Lotte Mason
Mrs Molly Meacher
Dr Eric Mendelson
Mr Howard McClarron
Mr Brian McGinnis
Mrs Inge Midforth
Mr Alan Milligan
Dr Ihsan Mian
Mr Alban Morley
Mr Simon Mumford
Prof. Elaine Murphy
Mr T.M. Napier
Dr David Neal
Miss Iris Nutting
Mrs Jeraine Olsen
Mrs Elizabeth Owen
Dr Femi Oyebode

Mr Alan Parkin
Mrs Marisa Phillips
Dr Robin Philpott
Ms Julia Prior
Dr Gwyn Pryce
Dr John Rao
Mrs Elaine Rassaby
Mrs Geneure Richardson
Mrs Mair Roberts
Ms Jenny Rogers
Dr Martyn Rowton-Lee
Mrs Anita Samuels
Ms Lucy Scott-Moncrieff
Dr Poppy Sebaratnam
Mrs Christine Selim
Mr John Sharich
Ms Lydia Sinclair
Mr Brian Smith
Ms Penny Spinks
Mr Ray Stables
Mrs Beryl Stroll
Mr Michael Taylor
Mr Harry Teaney
Mr Brian Thorne
Mr David Torpy
Mr Alan Watson
Prof. Donald West
Mr Alistair Williamson
Mr Len Wilson
Mr Ron Wix
Prof. Aubrey Yates
Dr Tony Zigmond

APPENDIX 2

EXTRACTS FROM MENTAL HEALTH ACT 1983

General protection of detained patients

120.—(1) The Secretary of State shall keep under review the exercise of the powers and the discharge of the duties conferred or imposed by this Act so far as relating to the detention of patients or to patients liable to be detained under this Act and shall make arrangements for persons authorised by him in that behalf—

(a) to visit and interview in private patients detailed under this Act in hospitals and mental nursing homes; and

(b) to investigate—
  (i) any complaint made by a person in respect of a matter that occurred while he was detained under this Act in a hospital or mental nursing home and which he considers has not been satisfactorily dealt with by the managers of that hospital or mental nursing home; and

  (ii) any other complaint as to the exercise of the powers or the discharge of the duties conferred or imposed by this Act in respect of a person who is or has been so detained.

(2) The arrangements made under this section in respect of the investigation of complaints may exclude matters from investigation in specified circumstances and shall not require any person exercising functions under the arrangements to undertake or continue with any investigation where he does not consider it appropriate to do so.

(3) Where any such complaint as is mentioned in subsection (1)(b)(ii) above is made by a Member of Parliament and investigated under the arrangements made under this section the results of the investigation shall be reported to him.

(4) For the purpose of any such review as it mentioned in subsection (1) above or of carrying out his functions under arrangements made under this section any person authorised in that behalf by the Secretary of State may at any reasonable time—

(a) visit and interview and, if he is a registered medical practitioner, examine in private any patient in a mental nursing home; and

(b) require the production of and inspect any records relating to the detention or treatment of any person who is or has been detained in a mental nursing home.

(5) [*Repealed by the Registered Homes Act* 1984, *s.*57(3), *Sched.* 3.]

(6) The Secretary of State may make such provision as he may with the approval of the Treasury determine for the payment of remuneration allowances, pensions or gratuities to or in respect of persons exercising functions in relation to any such review as is mentioned in subsection (1) above or functions under arrangements made under this section.

Mental Health Act Commission

121.—(1) Without prejudice to section 126(3) of the National Health Service Act 1977 (powers to vary or revoke orders or directions) there shall continue to be a special health authority known as the Mental Health Act Commission established under section 11 of that Act.

(2) Without prejudice to the generality of his powers under section 13 of that Act, the Secretary of State shall direct the Commission to perform on his behalf—

(a) the function of appointing registered medical practitioners for the purposes of Part IV of this Act and section 118 above and of appointing other persons for the purposes of section 57(2)(a) above; and

(b) the functions of the Secretary of State under sections 61 and 120(1) and (4) above.

(3) The registered medical practitioners and other persons appointed for the purposes mentioned in subsection (2)(a) above may include members of the Commission.

(4) The Secretary of State may, at the request of or after consultation with the Commission and after consulting such other bodies as appear to him to be concerned, direct the Commission to keep under review the care and treatment, or any aspect of the care and treatment, in hospitals and mental nursing homes of patients who are not liable to be detained under this Act.

(5) For the purpose of any such review as is mentioned in subsection (4) above any person authorised in that behalf by the Commission may at any reasonable time—

(a) visit and interview and, if he is a registered medical practitioner, examine in private any patient in a mental nursing home; and

(b) require the production of and inspect any records relating to the treatment of any person who is or has been a patient in a mental nursing home.

(6) The Secretary of State may make such provision as he may with the approval of the Treasury determine for the payment of remuneration, allowances, pensions or gratuities to or in respect of persons exercising functions in relation to any such review as is mentioned in subsecton (4) above.

(7) The Commission shall review any decision to withhold a postal packet (or anything contained in it) under subsection (1)(b) or (2) of section 134 below if any application in that behalf is made—

(a) in a case under subsection (1)(b) by the patient; or

(b) in a case under subsection (2), either by the patient of by the person by whom the postal packet was sent;

and any such application shall be made within six months of the receipt by the applicant of the notice referred to in subsection (6) of that section.

(8) On an application under subsection (7) above the Commission may direct that the postal packet which is the subject of the application (or anything contained in it) shall not be withheld and the managers in question shall comply with any such direction.

(9) The Secretary of State may by regulations make provision with respect to the making and determination of applications under subsection (7) above, including provision for the production to the Commission of any postal packet which is the subject of such an application.

(10) The Commission shall in the second year after its establishment and subsequently in every second year publish a report on its activities; and copies of every such report shall be sent by the Commission to the Secretary of State who shall lay a copy before each House of Parliament.

(11) Paragraph 9 of Schedule 5 to the said Act of 1977 (pay and allowances for chairmen and members of health authorities) shall have effect in relation to the Mental Health Act Commission as if references in sub-paragraphs (1) and (2) to the Chairman included references to any member and as if sub-paragraphs (4) and (5) were omitted.

1983 No. 892

NATIONAL HEALTH SERVICE, ENGLAND AND WALES

The Mental Health Act Commission (Establishment and Constitution) Order 1983

Made – – – –	*17th June* 1983
Laid before Parliament	*1st July* 1983
Coming into Operation	
Articles 1, 2 and 4	*1st September* 1983
Remainder	*30th September* 1983

The Secretary of State for Social Services, in exercise of the powers conferred upon him by section 11 of the National Health Service Act 1977(*a*), and of all other powers enabling him in that behalf, hereby makes the following order:

Citation, commencement and interpretation

1.—(1) This order may be cited as the Mental Health Act Commission (Establishment and Constitution) Order 1983 and shall come into operation on 1st September 1983 except that Article 3 shall come into operation on 30th September 1983.

(2) In this order—

"the Act" means the Mental Health Act 1983(b);

"the Commission" means the Commission established by Article 2 of this Order.

Establishment of the Commission

2. There is hereby established a special health authority which shall be known as the Mental Health Act Commission.

Functions of the Commission

3.—(1) Subject to and in accordance with such directions as the Secretary of State may give to the Commission, the Commission shall, in addition to performing its functions specified in the Act, perform on behalf of the Secretary of State the functions specified in paragraph (2) of this Article and such other functions as the Secretary of State may direct.

(**a**) 1977 c. 49; section 11(1) was amended by the Health Services Act 1980 (c. 53), Schedule 1, paragraph 31.
(**b**) 1983 c. 20.

(2) the functions of the Secretary of State referred to in paragraph (1) above are—

(a) the function of appointing registered medical practitioners for the purposes of Part IV of the Act (consent to treatment) and section 118 of the Act (practitioners required to certify consent and to give second opinion) and of appointing other persons for the purposes of section 57(2)(a) of the Act (persons required to certify consent);

(b) the functions of the Secretary of State under section 61 of the Act (review of treatment);

(c) the functions of the Secretary of State under section 120(1) and (4) of the Act (general protection of patients detained under the Act); and

(d) the function of submitting to the Secretary of State proposals as to the content of the code of practice which he shall prepare, and from time to time revise, under section 118(1) of the Act, and in particular to propose, for the purposes of section 118(2) of the Act, forms of medical treatment in addition to any specified in regulations made for the purposes of section 57 of the Act which in the opinion of the Commission give rise to special concern.

Constitution of the Commission

4. The Commission shall consist of such number of members as the Secretary of State may from time to time determine of whom one shall be the chairman and one vice-chairman.

Norman Fowler,
Secretary of State for Social Services.

17th June 1983.

EXPLANATORY NOTE

(*This Note is not part of the Order.*)

This Order provides for the establishment, as required by section 56(1) of the Mental Health (Amendment) Act 1982 (c. 51), and the constitution of a special health authority, to be known as the Mental Health Act Commission, to exercise functions under the Mental Health Act 1983, including the appointment of medical practitioners and other persons for the purposes of that Act, the review of treatment, the general protection of patients detained under that Act and the submission to the Secretary of State of proposals for the preparation and revision of a Code of Practice.

1983 No. 894

NATIONAL HEALTH SERVICE, ENGLAND AND WALES

The Mental Health Act Commission Regulations 1983

Made	*17th June* 1983
Laid before Parliament	*1st July* 1983
Coming into Operation	*1st September* 1983

The Secretary of State for Social Services, in exercise of the powers conferred upon him by paragraph 12 of Schedule 5 to the National Health Service Act 1977(**a**), and of all other powers enabling him in that behalf, hereby makes the following regulations:—

Citation, commencement and interpretation

1.—(1) These regulations may be cited as the Mental Health Act Commission Regulations 1983 and shall come into operation on 1st September 1983.

(2) In these regulations, unless the context otherwise requires—

"the Commission" means the Mental Health Act Commission established by the Order;

"the Order" means the Mental Health Act Commission (Establishment and Constitution) Order 1983(**b**).

Appointment of chairman and members

2. The chairman and members of the Commission shall be appointed by the Secretary of State.

Tenure of office of chairman and members

3. Subject to the following provisions of these regulations and to any provisions of regulations applied by these regulations, the term of office of the chairman or a member shall be such period, not exceeding four years, as the Secretary of State may specify on making the appointment.

Termination of tenure of office

4.—(1) The chairman or a member of the Commission may resign his office at any time during the period for which he was appointed by giving notice in writing to the Secretary of State.

(**a**) 1977 c. 49.   (**b**) S.I. 1983/892.

(2) Notwithstanding that the appointment of the chairman or any member is for a term of years, the Secretary of State may, at any time, terminate that person's tenure of office.

Eligibility for re-appointment
5. Subject to any provisions of regulations applied by these regulations as to disqualification from membership, the chairman or a member of the Commission shall, on the termination of his tenure of office, be eligible for re-appointment.

Vice-chairman
6.—(1) The Secretary of State may appoint a member of the Commission to be vice-chairman for such period as the Secretary of State may specify on making the appointment.

(2) Where no such appointment is made, the chairman and members of the Commission shall elect one of their number, other than the chairman, to be vice-chairman for a period of one year or, where the period of his membership during which he is elected has less than a year to run, for the remainder of such period.

(3) Any members so appointed or elected may at any time resign from the office of vice-chairman by giving notice in writing—

> (a) if he was appointed by the Secretary of State, to the Secretary of State;

> (b) in any other case, to the chairman of the Commission,

and the Secretary of State may thereupon appoint another member or, failing such an appointment, the chairman and members shall thereupon elect another member as vice-chairman in accordance with paragraph (1) or, as the case may be, paragraph (2) of this regulation.

Committees and sub-committees
7.—(1) The Secretary of State shall appoint a central policy committee of the Commission, consisting wholly of members of the Commission, but the Commission may co-opt any other member of the Commission as a member of the committee.

(2) Subject to paragraph (3) of this regulation and subject to and in accordance with such directions as the Secretary of State may give to that committee, the central policy committee shall perform on behalf of the Commission the following functions:—

> (a) the function mentioned in Article 3(2)(*d*) of the Order (proposals for the code of practice);

> (b) the preparation of the report on the Commission's activities required by section 121(10) of the Mental Health Act 1983(*a*);

> (c) any other function, or activity in connection with any function, which the Commission may require it to perform.

(**a**) S.I. 1983 c. 20.

(3) The functions mentioned in paragraph (2)(*a*) and (*b*) of this regulation, and any such function under paragraph (2)(*c*) of this regulation as the Commission may specify, shall be performed in consultation with the Commission.

(4) Subject to such directions as may be given by the Secretary of State, the Commission may, and if so directed shall, appoint committees of the Commission, consisting wholly of members of the Commission.

(5) A committee appointed under this regulation may, subject to such directions as may be given by the Secretary of State or the Commission appoint sub-committees consisting wholly of members of the Commission.

(6) Any power in this regulation to appoint members of the Commission as members of any committee or sub-committee shall include the power to appoint the chairman as a member of such a committee or sub-committee.

Meetings and proceedings
8.—(1) The meetings and proceedings of the Commission shall be conducted in accordance with Standing Orders made under paragraph (2) of this regulation.

(2) Subject to paragraph (3) of this regulation, the Commission shall make, and may vary or revoke, Standing Orders for the regulation of their proceedings and business and provision may be made in those Standing Orders for the suspension of those Orders.

(3) The Standing Orders shall provide that there shall be held at least one full meeting of the Commission in any year.

Application of regulations relating to membership
9. The provisions of regulation 7 (disqualification for appointment) and regulation 8 (cessation of disqualification) of the National Health Service (Regional and District Health Authorities: Membership and Procedure) Regulations 1983(a) shall apply as if any reference in those regulations to an Authority included a reference to the Commission.

Norman Fowler,
Secretary of State for Social Services.

(a) S.I. 1983/315.

APPENDIX 3

NATIONAL STANDING COMMITTEES TERMS OF REFERENCE

Research and Information

1. To monitor and keep under review the Commission's arrangements for the storage and handling of information arising from its own work; and make proposals for its improvement.

2. To initiate proposals for research or monitoring activities, or receive them from within and outside the MHAC, and to comment upon them.

3. To oversee the collation of material for the preparation and publication of the Biennial Report.

4. To undertake other relevant tasks as are referred to it by the Commission, the Central Policy Committee (CPC) or the Chief Executive.

Visiting

1. To study the pattern of Commission visits to hospitals and to monitor such visits.

2. To develop procedures to improve the Commission's practice in undertaking this task.

3. To advice the Commission on issues arising out of undertaking visits where they are not better dealt with by another National Standing Committee (NSC).

4. To prepare material for the Biennial Report.

5. To undertake other relevant tasks referred to it by the Commission, CPC of the Chief Executive.

Learning Disabilities

1. To study and keep under review all aspects of the care and treatment of and services for people who—

   (a) suffer from learning disabilities with psychiatric illness or who are behaviourally disturbed

   (b) Non-volitional patients.

2. To advise the Commission on issues relating to these groups of patients.

3. To contribute to the effective undertaking by the Commission of its statutory remit in relation to these groups of patients.

4. To prepare material for the Biennial Report.

5. To undertake all the relevant tasks referred to it by the Commission, CPC or the Chief Executive.

Legal and Parliamentary Affairs

1. To establish liaison with relevant parliamentary committees and/or MPs.

2. To monitor legal and parliamentary developments and activities that are relevant to the Commission's work.

3. To advise the Commission on legal problems with the 1983 Mental Health Act and related legislation.

4. To monitor legal "opinions/advice" given by the Commission and develop procedures to improve the practice of Commissioners and staff.

5. To prepare material for the Biennial Report.

6. To undertake other relevant tasks referred to it by the Commission, CPC or the Chief Executive.

Code of Practice

1. To keep under review the Commission's monitoring of the implementation of the Mental Health Act Code of Practice and contribute to the development of procedures to improve the practice of Commissioners in undertaking that task.

2. To advise the CPC and the Commission on issues relating to the meaning and application of the Code in particular any part of the Code that requires revision and in relation to which the Commission should consider making recommendations to the Secretary of State.

3. To prepare material for the Biennial Report.

4. To undertake other relevant tasks referred to it by the Commission, CPC or the Chief Executive.

Community Care

1. To study and keep under review this provision within the community of treatment and care to people with mental health problems.

2. To monitor Commission meetings with Social Service Departments and to develop procedures to improve the practices of the Commission in undertaking such tasks.

3. To advice the CPC and Commission on issues relating to community care.

4. To prepare relevant material for the Biennial Report.

5. To undertake other relevant tasks referred to it by the Commission, CPC or the Chief Executive.

Race and Culture

1. To study and report on issues of race and culture as they relate to the Commission's work.

2. To advise the CPC and the Commission on relevant issues and to contribute to the promotion of a greater understanding within the Commission of matters relevant to race and culture and the development of Commission policies, procedures and practice that reflects that understanding.

3. To monitor the implementation of any policy promulgated by and for the Commission and to make proposals for updating where necessary.

4. To prepare material for the Biennial Report.

5. To undertake other relevant tasks as referred to it by the Commission, CPC or the Chief Executive.

Mentally Disordered Offenders

1. To study and monitor the provisions for the care and treatment of and services for "difficult and offender patients" with mental health problems.

2. To advise the CPC and the Commission on issues or concerns relating to this group of patients.

3. To contribute to the effective undertaking by the Commission of its statutory tasks in relation to this group of patients.

4. To prepare material for the Biennial Report.

5. To undertake other relevant tasks referred to it by the Commission, CPC or the Chief Executive.

Consent to Treatment

1. To monitor the Commission's undertaking of its responsibilities in relation to Part IV of the Mental Health Act 1983.

2. To develop procedures to improve practice in relation to the undertaking of such responsibilities.

3. To advise the CPC and the Commission on issues arising out of the undertaking of such responsibilities or which are otherwise relevant to consent to treatment generally.

4. To prepare material for the Biennial Report.

5. To undertake other relevant tasks as referred to it by the Commission, CPC or the Chief Executive.

Complaints

1. To monitor the Commission's investigation of complaints pursuant to Section 120(1)(b) and to develop procedures to improve the Commission's practice.

2. To advice the CPC and the Commission on issues of concern arising out of such activities where they are not better dealt with by another NSC.

3. To prepare material for the Biennial Report.

4. To undertake other relevant tasks as referred to it by the Commission, CPC or the Chief Executive.

APPENDIX 4

COMMISSION EXPENDITURE 1April 1989–30 March 1993

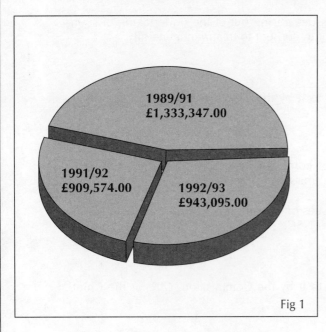

Fig 1

Commissioner Fees and Expenses

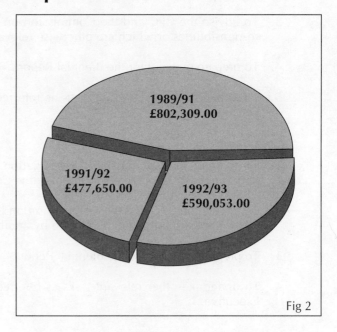

Fig 2

Second Opinion Doctors Fees and Expenses

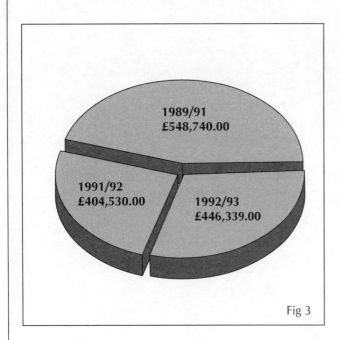

Fig 3

Staff Salaries

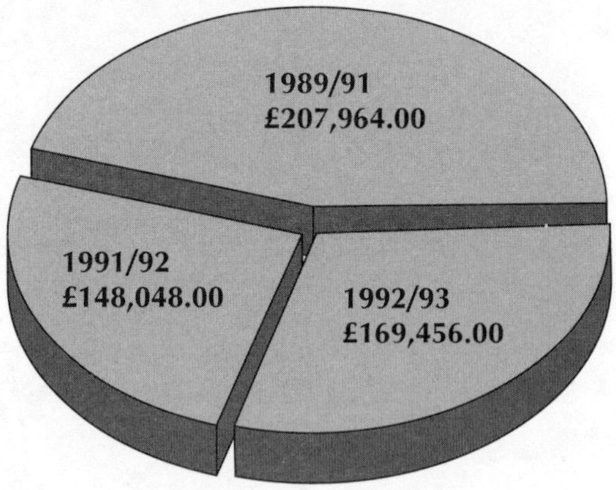

Fig 4

Non-manpower Expenditure

TOTAL COMMISSION EXPENDITURE

1 April 1989–30 March 1993

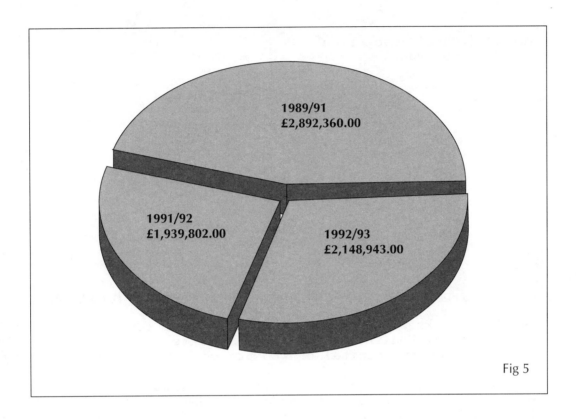

1989/91
£2,892,360.00

1991/92
£1,939,802.00

1992/93
£2,148,943.00

Fig 5

APPENDIX 5

Letters which have been circulated to all Health Authorities, Trusts, Registered Mental
Nursing Homes and Social Services Departments

Mental Health Act Commission

From the Chief Executive

Maid Marian House 56 Hounds Gate Nottingham NG1 6BG
Tel: 0602 504040 Fax: 0602 505998

To: All Chief Executives
of NHS Trusts

31st January 1992

Dear Chief Executive

Deaths of patients detained under the 1983 Mental Health Act.

As you will know the Commission keeps under review the operation
of the Mental Health Act 1983 as it relates to patients detained
under the Act in hospital or who are on leave in the community.

In pursuit of its responsibilities the Commission from time to time
**reminds relevant organisations of its standing request that it be
informed of the death of any detained patient as soon as possible
after it has occurred and that it also be advised at the earliest
opportunity of the date and venue of any resulting inquest.** It is
usual Commission practice for a Commissioner to attend such
inquests as an observer.

Where your trust is responsible for facilities containing patients
detained under the Act I would be very grateful if you would
acknowledge receipt and confirm that such facilities and all
relevant personnel are aware of this request and that it will be
acted upon should the necessity arise.

Yours faithfully

William Bingley

Mental Health Act Commission

From the Chief Executive

Maid Marian House 56 Hounds Gate Nottingham NG1 6BG
Tel: 0602 504040 Fax: 0602 505998

To: All General Managers and
Chief Executives
of Health Authorities

31st January 1992

Dear Sir or Madam

Deaths of patients detained under the 1983 Mental Health Act.

As you will know the Commission keeps under review the operation of the Mental Health Act 1983 as it relates to patients detained under the Act in hospital or who are on leave in the community.

In pursuit of its responsibilities the Commission from time to time **reminds health authorities of its standing request that it be informed of the death of any detained patient as soon as possible after they occur and that it also be advised at the earliest opportunity of the date and venue of any resulting inquest.** It is usual Commission practice for a Commissioner to attend such inquests as an observer.

Where your authority is directly managing facilities containing patients detained under the Act I would be very grateful if you would acknowledge receipt and that this request is drawn to the attention of such facilities and all relevant staff.

Where your authority is purchasing care for patients detained under the 1983 Act from NHS Trusts or the non-statutory sector please would you as purchasers ensure that the providers of such services are aware of this request. The Commission would be grateful if you would monitor the providers compliance with the Commission's request and would be further grateful if you would consider incorporating compliance with this request in any contract or agreement with your providers.

Yours faithfully

William Bingley

Mental Health Act Commission

Maid Marian House 56 Hounds Gate Nottingham NG1 6BG
Tel: 0602 504040 Fax: 0602 505998

From the Chief Executive

To: The registered proprietors
     of all Mental Nursing Homes

31st January 1992

Dear Sir or Madam

Death of patients detained under the 1983 Mental Health Act.

As you will know the Commission keeps under review the operation
of the Mental Health Act 1983 as it relates to patients detained
under the Act in hospital or who are on leave in the community.

In pursuit of its responsibilities the Commission from time to time
**reminds relevant organisations of its standing request that it be
informed of the death of any detained patient as soon as possible
after it has occurred and that it also be advised at the earliest
opportunity of the date and venue of any resulting inquest.** It is
usual Commission practice for a Commissioner to attend such
inquests as an observer.

I would be grateful if you would acknowledge receipt of this letter
and confirm that all relevant personnel are aware of this request
and that it will be acted upon should the necessity arise.

Yours faithfully

William Bingley

Mental Health Act Commission

From the Chief Executive

Maid Marian House 56 Hounds Gate Nottingham NG1 6BG
Tel: 0602 504040 Fax: 0602 505998

To: General Managers and
Chief Executives of District Health Authorities

29th January 1992

Dear Sir or Madam

MENTAL NURSING HOMES REGISTERED UNDER SECTION 23 (3) (c) OF THE REGISTERED HOMES ACT TO RECEIVE PATIENTS DETAINED UNDER THE MENTAL HEALTH ACT.

As you will know, the Commission has a duty to visit Mental Nursing Homes registered to receive detained patients as described above.

In pursuit of our undertaking of these responsibilities we need to ensure that our records of such homes are updated. I should be most grateful if you would arrange for the Commission to receive details of any such homes currently registered by your authority under the above sub-section of the Act, so that the information we currently hold can be checked. It would be very helpful if we could be supplied with a copy of the registration certificate in each case.

Please may I take this opportunity of reminding your authority that it would be a great assistance to the Commission if we could be notified of any new registrations as well as any de-registrations.

If you have any queries regarding these requests please do not hesitate to contact me.

Your assistance in this matter will be greatly appreciated.

Yours faithfully

William Bingley

A response by 28th February 1992 would be very helpful.

Mental Health Act Commission

From the Chief Executive

Maid Marian House 56 Hounds Gate Nottingham NG1 6BG
Tel: 0602 504040 Fax: 0602 505998

Our ref:- AC\MISC\LEGAL-2\MP

27 October 1992

TO:-   ALL GENERAL MANAGERS OR CHIEF EXECUTIVES OF
         HEALTH AUTHORITIES
         CHIEF EXECUTIVES OF NHS TRUSTS
         MANAGERS OF MENTAL NURSING HOMES
         DIRECTORS OF SOCIAL SERVICES DEPARTMENTS

Dear Sir/Madam

**PROVISION OF ADVICE ON LAW/PRACTICE BY MENTAL HEALTH ACT
COMMISSION**

Since the Commission was set up, it has received numerous
requests for advice and guidance on issues relating to the
Mental Health Act. Many of these enquiries, made by
telephone, involve complex issues of law and practice.

While the Commission wishes to be helpful in discussing
problems, it must be recognised that the Commission has no
statutory right to give formal legal advice. The responsibility for the correct interpretation of the law must remain with
those exercising powers under the Act and their legal
advisers. The Commission should not be consulted as an
alternative to obtaining formal legal advice.

Subject to this proviso - and because of the considerable
pressure on Commission staff - it would be helpful if, in
future, requests for a Commission view (unless extremely
urgent) are put in writing so that a considered response can
be given. Although slower, this more formal mechanism should
in the long term be more satisfactory for all concerned as it
should result in a more detailed and consistent view of which
there is some record.

I would be grateful if you bring this to the attention of the
appropriate managers and professionals, including those who
work directly with patients liable to be detained under the
Act.

Please find attached a list of essential publications to which
we feel those implementing the Act should have easy access.

Yours faithfully

WILLIAM BINGLEY
Chief Executive

Mental Health Act (1983) Chapter 20 — Reprinted 1988
Pub: HMSO, London
ISBN 0 10 542083 2

Mental Health Act (1983)
Memorandum on Parts I to VI, VIII and X
Pub: HMSO, London
ISBN 0 11 321078 7

The Mental Health (Hospital, Guardianship & Consent to Treatment) Regulations 1983
No. 893 — Reprinted 1988
Pub: HMSO, London
ISBN 0 11 036893 2

Jones R (1991)
Mental Health Act Manual [3rd Edition]
Pub: Sweet and Maxwell, London
ISBN 0 421 45170 X

The Code of Practice (Revised edition 1993)
Pub: HMSO, London
ISBN 0 11 321624 6

Mental Health (Scotland) Act (1984) Chapter 36
Pub: HMSO, London
ISBN 0 10 543684 4

The Mental Health Act Commission (1991)
Fourth Biennial Report: 1989–1991
Pub: HMSO, London
ISBN 0 11 321483 9

Gostin L (1983)
A Practical Guide to Mental Health Law: The Mental Health Act (1983) and related legislation
Pub: MIND Publications, London
ISBN 0 90055 59 1

Gunn M J (1991) [3rd]
Sex and the Law — a brief guide for staff working with people with learning difficulties
Pub: The Family Planning Association, London
ISBN 0 903289 41 5

Hoggett B (1990)
Mental Health Law 3rd Edition
Pub: Sweet and Maxwell, London
ISBN 0 421 42570 9

APPENDIX 6

Number of visits undertaken to Mental Health Units and meetings with Social Services Departments
July 1st 1991 to June 30th 1993

	Number of Visits	% of Total
Hospitals	1,089	69.5%
Special Hospitals	259	16.5%
Registered Mental Nursing Homes	34	2.2%
Social Services Departments	184	11.8%
TOTALS	1,566	100%

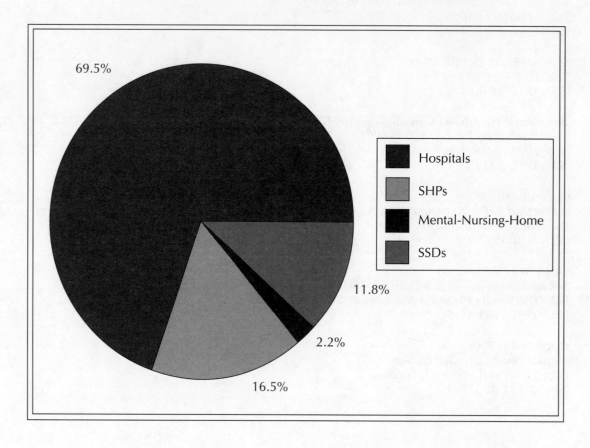

	Number of Unannounced Visits	Number of out of hours visits
Hospitals	3	4
Registered Mental Nursing Homes	3	0
TOTALS	6	4

APPENDIX 7

HEALTH OF THE NATION KEY AREA HANDBOOK 1993 — MENTAL ILLNESS

Contracting for Patients detained under the Mental Health Act 1983

The following are suggested paragraphs prepared by the Mental Health Act Commission for inclusion in contracts or service agreements covering services which will or may include services for patients detained under the Mental Health Act 1983.

a. The appropriate requirements and procedures contained in the Mental Health Act 1983 (the Act) and the Regulations made under the authority for that Act shall be complied with in respect of any person to whom the Act applies whilst a patient is receiving services under this contract/service agreement.

b. Reports shall be submitted at the required intervals to the Mental Health Act Commission in accordance with powers delegated to it by the Secretary of State in fulfilment of his responsibilities under Section 61 of the Act in respect of patients to whom this section applies.

c. The statutory "Managers" as defined in the Act (the district health authority or directors of the Trust) will ensure that their responsibilities:

   i.   to review the continued detention of patients in respect of whom the Responsible Medical Officer has submitted a report in accordance with Section 20 of the Act.

   ii. in the exercise of their powers of discharge under Section 23 of the act to consider requests by detained patients for a review of their detention;

   are delegated to a *committee or sub-committee of the authority which shall include only non-executive members and be properly authorised in accordance with Section 23(4) of the Act. Non-executive and any co-opted members should be suitably experienced or receive training.

   They will also ensure that their other statutory powers and duties are clearly delegated to competent officers and properly fulfilled.

d. The guidance contained in the Code of Practice issued by the Secretary of State in accordance with Section 118 of the Act together with any subsequent amendments and additions shall be observed as minimum standards.

e. In addition to compliance with the requirements of the Hospital Complaints Procedure Act, 1986 arrangements should be made to handle complaints from mentally disordered people which recognise that their state of mind may prevent them from formulating complaints or may lead to valid complaints being regarded as a manifestation of their condition.

f. The death of any person which occurs whilst detained under the provisions of the Mental Health Act, 1983 shall immediately be notified to the Mental Health Act Commission. Copies of reports for any inquest and arising from any investigation into the circumstances surrounding the death should be provided to the Commission together with the date of any inquest.

g. No patient covered by this contract/service agreement shall be disadvantaged of suffer adverse discrimination in any aspect of their care or treatment as consequence of cultural, racial or sexual characteristics, or any form of handicap and the requirements of relevant legislation must be observed.

*   In the case of NHS Trusts at the time of publication, legal advice is that the current definition of managers requires the function of discharging patients to be performed by three or more Non-executive Directors (one of whom may be the Chairman) in person. The Department has written to Trusts to explain this more fully (TEL 93/2). It will be seeking the earliest possible amendment to the Act to permit delegation to a committee;

Ref:C:\DATA\BIENNIAL\APPENDIX\12

APPENDIX 8

THE SPECIAL HOSPITAL VISITING POLICY

Aims and Objectives

The Commissions visiting programme for the Special Hospitals should:—

1. ensure that the rights and interests of Special Hospital patients are effectively safeguarded;

2. ensure that every patient in the Special Hospitals is contacted by Commissioners at least once a year;

3. be cost-effective within the resources allocated by the Central Policy Committee (CPC); and

4. be subject to consultation with the Special Hospitals Service Authority before adoption by the Commission.

Principles

The following principles are recommended:

5. Visiting Commissioners should relate to clinical units to facilitate communication with wards, nursing managers, responsible medical officers, and other clinical services.

6. The Commission should be organised to interact effectively with the clinical staff, the clinical teams, the Hospital Advisory Committees, the Hospital Management Teams and Special Hospitals Service Authority.

Practical Implementation

Special Hospital Panels.

7. All Commissioners should be expected to make a substantial commitment to the visiting programme for the Special Hospitals.

8. Each Commissioner should be allocated to one of the Special Hospital Panels (SHP), the number in each SHP being proportional to the number of patients in the Special Hospital for which they have responsibility. Each SHP will appoint a convenor.

9. A system should be established for determining the availability of Commissioners for Special Hospital Visits, to synchronise with the visits to hospitals and meetings with social services departments carried out by Commission Visiting Teams.

10. A system should be devised for inducting new members of each SHP, including orientation visits to the relevant Special Hospital.

11. (a) It is the policy of the Commission to make "out of hours" and "unannounced" visits;

(b) the relevant SHP convenors will decide when such visits should be made and shall inform the Chief Executive.

Visiting Team

12. Each SHP should be divided into visiting teams, depending upon the requirements of the units to be visited. Each visiting team should choose its own leader.

13. SHPs should meet at least on the occasion of each Commission meeting and review general issues in respect of the Special Hospital with which they are concerned. Each should make decisions as necessary, from time to time as to the composition of its teams and their allocation to units and responsibility in respect of particular departments and non-ward areas.

14. Each visiting team should be responsible for reviewing the documentation relating to the patient's detention, and for monitoring the implementation and recording of Part IV of the Act within its clinical units.

15. The visiting teams should also visit systematically non-ward areas as determined by their respective SHP's, e.g. rehabilitation workshops, schools, etc., according to an agreed protocol to ensure a consistent approach.

16. The visiting team should meet the clinical teams of the relevant clinical units at the closing meeting of the visit, unless there are special reasons for cancelling the final meeting. At such meetings, only issues which can be dealt with at ward level will be raised.

Team Convenors

17. Within the budget determined by the CPC the frequency of visiting to the units or wards of the Special Hospital should be decided by the team leaders for that hospital in conjunction with the SHP convenor.

18. Where it is thought necessary, the SHP convenor should ask CPC for an increased allocation of funded visiting days to meet special needs.

19. Each visiting team should consider the desirability both of out of hours and unannounced visits and if they think that such a visit is necessary, they should put a proposition for it through their leader to the convenor of the SHP.

20. The Team Leaders should meet at least once every six months other than at Commission meetings to share information, to monitor and evaluate the programme, to review complaints, to consider postal packets withheld, to prepare a report for the Hospital Management Team, to identify matters to be reported to the CPC and matters to be considered for the Biennial Report.

21. The formal meetings of the SHP should be supported by a member of staff.

22. The SHP convenor and complaints and visiting representatives of the SHP and visiting team leaders should meet with the HMT at least twice yearly.

23. Meetings at periodic intervals to be determined will also take place between each Hospital Advisory Committee and commissioners from the relevant SHP.

24. The SHP should identify matters to be discussed at the bianniel meeting between representatives of the Commission (including the Chairman) and the Special Hospitals Service Authority.

Clinical Units

25. To ensure that the visiting teams relate to appropriate clinical units, discussion should take place with the Hospital Management Team. The importance of the relationship with the responsible medical officer, and the other clinical staff should be stressed to ensure effective co-ordination in relation to transfer delays and consent to treatment issues.

26. To facilitate continuity of visiting, the hospital should be asked to notify the Commission when patients are transferred between wards, so that information on patients can be passed between visiting teams.

APPENDIX 9

COMPLAINTS POLICY

1. **The Statutory basis of the Commission's complaints remit**

   The statutory basis for the Commission's complaints remit is to be found at Section 120(1)(b) of the Act. There are two types of complaint that the Commission may investigate and guidance about them is set out in full in the guidelines (See paragraph 1 on page 10 in particular).

   Section 120(2) gives to the Commission the discretion not to investigate a complaint or to discontinue a complaint where it is appropriate to do so.

2. **Objectives of Complaints Policy**

   The aim of the Policy is to ensure that:

   (a) Complaints received by the Commission are properly identified as falling within or without Section 120;

   (b) Complaints are investigated promptly, effectively and fairly within a reasonable timescale (see paragraph 4 on page 4);

   (c) Where possible conciliation between Complainant and the individual organisation complained about is undertaken and a settlement acceptable to the Complainant and reasonable to the Commission, is achieved;

   (d) The Complainant is kept fully informed of the progress of the complaints investigation;

   (e) The result of the Commission's investigation and any recommendations are reported (in accordance with the guidance to be found at paragraph 9 on page 7 and para 24 page 16) to both the Complainant and those complained about; and

   (f) The Commission monitors the exercise of its complaints remit and in particular the achievement of the objectives set out above.

3. **Terminology**

   A complaint for the purpose of this procedure is any communication received by the Commission or any Commissioner which;

   (a) falls within the Commission complaints remit as set out in Section 120(1)(b) of the Act; and

   (b) In the case of such communications received by Commissioners while visiting hospitals or mental nursing homes cannot be satisfactorily resolved during the visit and require action to be taken after the conclusion of the visit.

   The definition includes complaints which merit investigation but cannot be investigated because the patient does not give or withdraws consent.

4. **Time limits**

   The following time limits should apply to Commission complaints investigations:

   (a) All complaints received in writing *will* be acknowledged in writing within two working days or receipt.

   (b) A more detailed response should be provided within three weeks of receipt of a Commission complaint. If this is not possible then an appropriate holding letter should be sent within that time.

(c) The investigation of most Commission complaints should be concluded within four-teen weeks. Where circumstances prevent the achievement of this objective, then the complainant should be informed and then kept further informed at not more than three weekly intervals; and

(d) Where the investigation of a Commission complaint is not concluded within twenty weeks of receipt of the complaint, then the matter should be referred to the Chief Executive for review.

In order to ensure that the investigation of complaints is carried out as promptly as possible, the time limits referred to above should be adhered to in as many investigations as possible. It is important, however, to ensure that compliance with the time limits is not to the detriment of the quality of the investigation. Where it is necessary to take longer than the time limits allow for, it is essential to keep the complainant informed.

APPENDIX 10

Total Number of Complaints received in each Category: * 1989–1991/1991–93 (1 July–30 June)

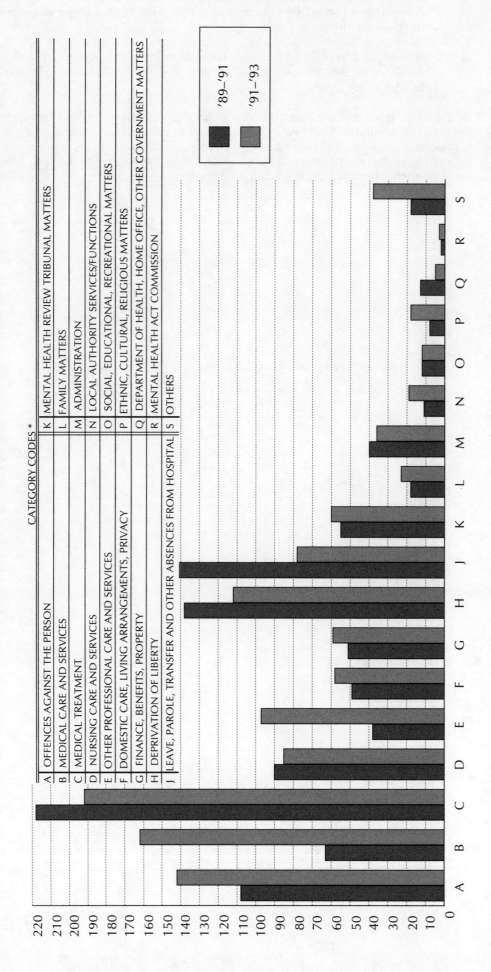

CATEGORY CODES *

A	OFFENCES AGAINST THE PERSON
B	MEDICAL CARE AND SERVICES
C	MEDICAL TREATMENT
D	NURSING CARE AND SERVICES
E	OTHER PROFESSIONAL CARE AND SERVICES
F	DOMESTIC CARE, LIVING ARRANGEMENTS, PRIVACY
G	FINANCE, BENEFITS, PROPERTY
H	DEPRIVATION OF LIBERTY
J	LEAVE, PAROLE, TRANSFER AND OTHER ABSENCES FROM HOSPITAL
K	MENTAL HEALTH REVIEW TRIBUNAL MATTERS
L	FAMILY MATTERS
M	ADMINISTRATION
N	LOCAL AUTHORITY SERVICES/FUNCTIONS
O	SOCIAL, EDUCATIONAL, RECREATIONAL MATTERS
P	ETHNIC, CULTURAL, RELIGIOUS MATTERS
Q	DEPARTMENT OF HEALTH, HOME OFFICE, OTHER GOVERNMENT MATTERS
R	MENTAL HEALTH ACT COMMISSION
S	OTHERS

'89–'91

'91–'93

Per cent of Complaints received in each Category: * 1989–1991/1991–93 (1 July–30 June)

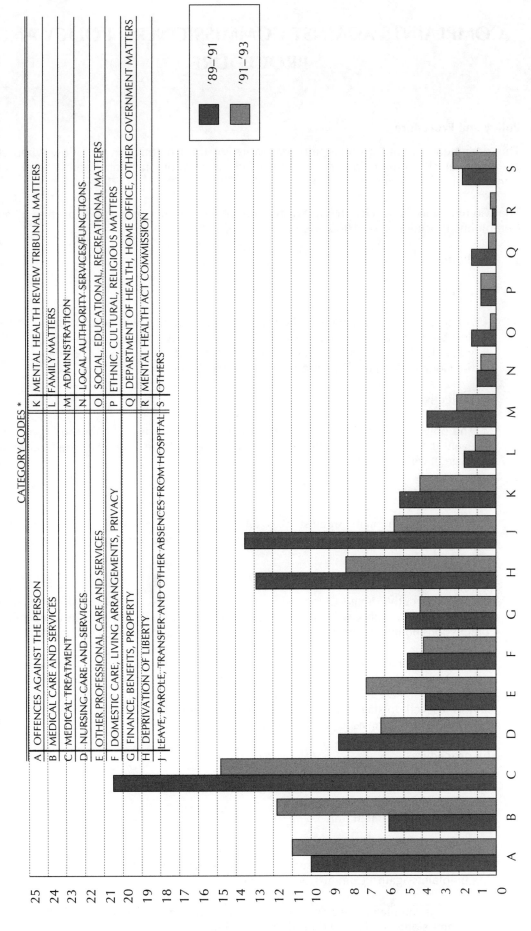

CATEGORY CODES *

A	OFFENCES AGAINST THE PERSON	K	MENTAL HEALTH REVIEW TRIBUNAL MATTERS
B	MEDICAL CARE AND SERVICES	L	FAMILY MATTERS
C	MEDICAL TREATMENT	M	ADMINISTRATION
D	NURSING CARE AND SERVICES	N	LOCAL AUTHORITY SERVICES/FUNCTIONS
E	OTHER PROFESSIONAL CARE AND SERVICES	O	SOCIAL, EDUCATIONAL, RECREATIONAL MATTERS
F	DOMESTIC CARE, LIVING ARRANGEMENTS, PRIVACY	P	ETHNIC, CULTURAL, RELIGIOUS MATTERS
G	FINANCE, BENEFITS, PROPERTY	Q	DEPARTMENT OF HEALTH, HOME OFFICE, OTHER GOVERNMENT MATTERS
H	DEPRIVATION OF LIBERTY	R	MENTAL HEALTH ACT COMMISSION
J	LEAVE, PAROLE, TRANSFER AND OTHER ABSENCES FROM HOSPITAL	S	OTHERS

■ '89–'91

■ '91–'93

APPENDIX 11

COMPLAINTS AGAINST COMMISSIONERS: POLICY AND PROCEDURE

Policy and Procedure

This document sets out a policy and procedure for the Commission to follow when complaints against Commissioners are received from complainants apart from other Commissioners or Commission staff.

The Commission is a Health Authority and therefore the provisions of the Hospital Complaints Procedures Act 1985 apply.

1. **The Policy**

   (a) **Preface**

   All complaints to which this Policy and Procedure applies will be considered seriously and promptly and investigated thoroughly and fairly. All complaints are potentially valuable indicators of the Commissions performance and provide pointers by which the Commissions quality of service can be measured.

   (b) **Objectives**

   The objective of this policy is reconciliation on the basis of established facts. In the event that this is not possible, then the vice Chairman (in Stage I) or the Chairman (in Stage II) will make a finding. (See below).

   (c) **Time limits**

   Save in exceptional circumstances all complaints investigation under this policy should be completed within six weeks of receipt of the complaint.

3. **Designated Officer**

   The Chief Executive is the Commissions 'designated Officer' to whom all complaints to which this policy refers will be referred. He will be responsible for ensuring that the Commissions policy and procedure is implemented in relation to each complaint received.

   In stage I (see below) of the procedure the Vice Chairman of the Commission will be informed of the progress of any complaints investigations and it will be the Vice Chairman and not be designated Officer who will make any provisional finding as to whether a complaint is justified. In stage II of the procedure it will be the Chairman who will (where necessary) make a finding as to whether a complaint is justified.

4. **The procedure**

   Stage I

   (a) **Receipt and initial action**

   All complaints received will be acknowledged by return and a copy of the complaints policy and procedure will be sent to the Complainant. All complaints will be allocated a complaints against Commissioner number.

   Where a complaint is received in writing, a copy of it will be sent immediately to the Commissioner/s concerned for their comments.

   Where a complaint is made verbally a transcript of the complaint will be sent immediately to:

i.   the Complainant to check for accuracy;

ii. the Commissioner concerned for their comments.

Where necessary the designated Officer (in consultation with the Vice Chairman) will seek further information.

(b) **Action after enquiries made**

i.   **Complaints report**

Once the designated Officer has received all the information referred to above, he will prepare a complaints report identifying any aspects of the complaint which are the subject of disagreement between the Complainant and the Commissioner concerned. On completion the designated Officer will refer this to the Vice Chairman;

ii. on receipt the Vice Chairman will decide if any further enquiries are necessary and if a meeting between the Complainant and the Commission/s concerned is necessary to clarify any unresolved matters or to seek a resolution.

At this stage the Vice Chairman will also offer a meeting to the Commissioner/s complained about.

iii. Once (ii) above is completed, then the Vice Chairman will further consider the matter and make a decision as to:

a.   whether the matter has been resolved and if so what action should be taken; or

b.   In the absence of resolution whether the complaint is justified and what action should be taken. Such a finding will be a *provisional finding*.

Where the Vice Chairman makes a provisional finding that the complaint is justified, then both the Complainant and the Commissioner/s concerned will be notified immediately about the finding together with (in broad outline) the reasons supporting the finding. Both complainant and Commissioner will be advised that if they are dissatisfied with the finding, then they may request that the matter be referred to *Stage II*.

Stage II

(a) Where the Complainant or Commissioner complained against disagrees with the provisional finding made by the Vice Chairman, then they should notify the designated Officer. On receipt of such notification the designated Officer will be to refer the matter to the Chairman, who will:

i.   where necessary call on a designated Officer to seek further information; and/or

ii. recommend a further meeting between the complainant and the Commissioners concerned. In order to clarify any misunderstandings, disputed facts or to seek a resolution of the matter.

(b) Where it is not possible to resolve the matter, the Chairman will then make a *finding* as to whether the complaint is justified and what action (if necessary) needs to be taken.

APPENDIX 12

Section 58 — Second Opinion Requests
July 1st 1991–June 30th 1993
MHA Category Totals

Table 1		%
Mental Illness	8,271	93.57
Mental Impairment	340	3.85
Severe Mental Impairment	80	0.91
Psychopathic Disorder	148	1.67
TOTALS	8,839	100

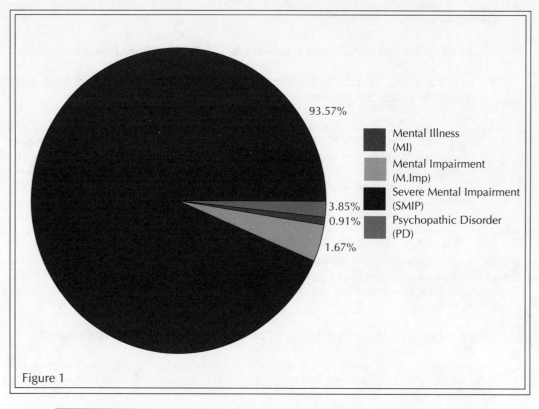

93.57%

Mental Illness (MI)

Mental Impairment (M.Imp)

Severe Mental Impairment (SMIP)

Psychopathic Disorder (PD)

3.85%

0.91%

1.67%

Figure 1

Table 2				
C.V.T	M.I	M.I.P	S.M.I	P.D
1	1,286	142	23	66
2	919	44	12	10
3	1,084	20	8	15
4	648	15	7	7
5	1,721	55	11	15
6	1,265	18	6	5
7	1,348	46	13	30
TOTAL	8,271	340	80	148
% OF TOTAL	93.57	3.85	0.91	1.67

Totals by Category of Mental disorder and Region

Table 3

R.H.A.	Mental Illness	Mental Impairment	Severe Mental Impairment	Psychopathic Disorder
East Anglia	374	64	6	7
N.E. Thames	648	23	2	14
Oxford	389	17	2	9
N.W. Thames	530	27	10	1
S.E. Thames	447	11	6	2
S.W. Thamees	409	9	2	7
Wessex	305	4	1	4
South Western	343	11	6	3
Northern	402	20	5	5
Yorkshire	731	21	4	7
Trent	588	14	2	3
West Midlands	861	16	5	2
Wales	404	2	1	3
North Western	871	17	3	3
Mersey	379	10	3	1
Special Hospitals Service Authority				
Ashworth Hospital	98	19	7	26
Broadmoor Hospital	228	0	0	6
Rampton Hospital	2264	55	15	45
TOTAL	8,271	340	80	148

Totals by gender and type of treatment

TABLE 4: Totals by Gender		
Male	4,010	45%
Female	4,829	55%
Total	8,839	100%

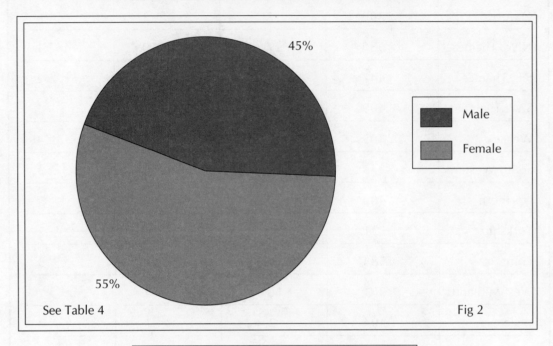

See Table 4   Fig 2

TABLE 5: Totals by type of treatment		
Medicines	4,627	52.3%
ECT	4,067	46%
Both	145	1.7%
Total	8,839	100%

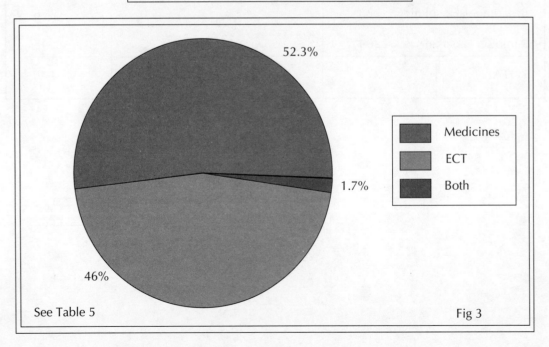

See Table 5   Fig 3

TABLE 6: (Mental Illness Category Only			
GENDER	FORM OF TREATMENT		
	Medication	ECT	Both
Male	2,546	1,263	54
Female	1,724	2,614	70
TOTAL	4,270	3,877	124
% OF TOTAL	51.6%	46.9%	1.5%

Totals by Section

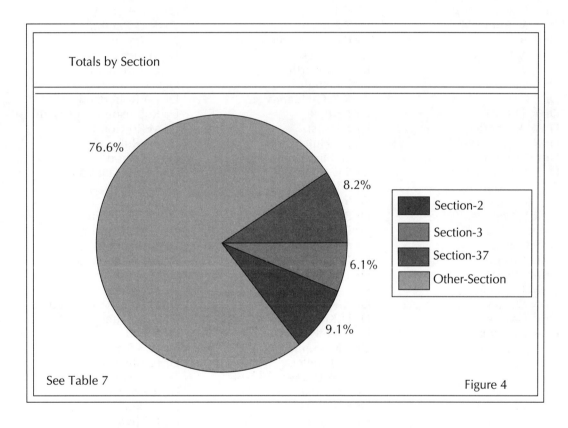

76.6%

8.2%

6.1%

9.1%

Section-2
Section-3
Section-37
Other-Section

See Table 7

Figure 4

TABLE 7: Totals by Section		
2	729	8.2%
3	6,767	76.6%
37	804	9.1%
Other	536	6.1%
Total	8,839	100%

APPENDIX 13

Sec 58 Appointed Doctors
July 1991–June 1993

Dr M T Abou-Saleh
Dr P Abraham
Dr J M Annear
Dr J A Barrett
Dr S Baxter
Dr S M Benbow
Dr M S Bethell
Dr K Bergman
Dr K G M Bhakta
Dr E Birchall
Dr A A Black
Prof R S. Bluglass
Dr N Bouras
Dr J Bolton
Dr C E Boyd
Dr A M Bradfield
Dr C Brook
Dr O V Briscoe
Dr A W Burke
Dr C Calvert
Dr E Carr
Dr M D Cashman
Dr W K Charles
Dr P C Chaudray
Dr I D Chisholm
Dr A D Clarkson
Dr J Cockburn
Dr I B Cookson
Dr R V Cope
Dr M W Cottrell
Dr S Craske
Dr D Cronin
Dr J Cuthill
Dr M H Davies
Dr N Davies
Dr C Davies
Dr K Davison
Dr K A Day
Dr R Devine
Dr D Dick
Dr D Dickens
Dr G O Duborg
Dr D L F Dunleavy
Dr H Eaton
Dr H Edwards
Dr A F Fairbarn
Dr M Faulk
Dr G S Feggetter
Dr T W Fenton
Dr E F Fenton
Dr S Fernando
Dr J Fisher
Dr M W Forth
Dr A F Francis
Dr T Garvey
Dr D Gaspar
Dr H Ghadiali
Dr A Ghosh
Dr C Ghosh
Dr N L Gittleson
Dr E B Gordon

Dr J Gordon-Russell
Dr M H P Green
Dr J S Grimshaw
Dr E M Gregg
Dr J D Hailstone
Dr K Hamadah
Dr M A Harper
Dr B G Harwin
Dr J A Harrington
Dr M T Haslam
Dr W A Heaton-Ward
Dr B E Heine
Dr P Hettiaratchy
Dr M Hill
Dr O Hill
Dr T Holland
Dr L I M A Homewood
Dr A Hauck
Dr E Howarth
Dr J S Hughes
Dr R K G Hughes
Dr J Hurst
Dr L Hurst
Dr J A Hutchinson
Dr G S Ibrahimi
Dr S R N James
Dr P M Jefferys
Dr Jenkins
Dr B John
Dr D V Jones
Dr A C Kaeser
Dr G Kanakaratnam
Dr T A Kerr
Dr A M P Kellam
Dr K Khan
Dr D Kohen
Dr H Kelly
Dr L M Kremer
Dr J E Langley
Dr M A Launer
Dr L I Liebling
Dr B A Lowe
Dr J S Lyon
Dr T Malcolm
Dr S Malik
Dr P Mars
Dr G N Mathur
Dr M Matthews
Dr J McConnell
Dr J McHugh
Dr A L McNeil
Dr L G Measey
Dr G Mehta
Dr I H Mian
Dr G Milner
Dr Minto
Dr A Morrell
Dr J D Mumford
Dr H Myers
Dr G Nanayakkara
Dr C D Neal

Dr T E Nelson
Dr R Neville
Dr J G Noble
Dr M O'Brien
Dr S Olivieri
Dr F Oyebode
Dr M A Palejwala
Dr S S Palia
Dr J E Phillips
Dr R M Phillpott
Dr B M W Pitt
Dr G Pryce
Dr P H Rack
Dr J Rao
Dr S C Rastogi
Dr N G Renton
Dr A Regan
Dr M Rice
Dr E H Richards
Dr J M Roberts
Dr J A Robertson
Dr Robinson (Deceased)
Dr M Rowton-Lee
Dr A J Rugg
Dr B Rathod
Dr T Rajamanickam
Dr P Saleem
Dr M A Salih
Dr P H Salmons
Dr G A Sampson
Dr P N Sarkar
Dr N P Seberatnum
Dr M Segal
Dr Silverman
Dr J J Slater (Deceased)
Dr Z T Slattery
Dr S Soni
Dr W S Stanley
Dr J S Stead
Dr D A Stephens
Dr R L Symonds
Dr L Tarlo
Dr R Thvasothy
Dr R Thaya-Paran
Dr R M Toms
Dr G D P Wallen
Dr M Way
Dr A M Walsh
Dr K F Weeks
Dr L R West
Dr J A Whitehead
Dr D Williams
Dr A M Wilson
Dr G C Wijeyratne
Dr W Wright
Dr A S Zigmond

APPENDIX 14

WITH-HOLDING OF MAIL AND COMMISSION REVIEW POWERS: POLICY AND PROCEDURE

A) Introduction

The powers of hospital managers to examine and with-hold postal packets and their duties when they exercise those powers, are set out in Section 134 of the Mental Health Act 1983 and the Mental Health (Hospital, Guardianship and Consent to Treatment) Regulations (S.1 1983 No. 893). Where a packet or anything contained in it is with-held the duties include one to notify within seven days, the patient and, if known, the person by whom the packet was sent, of a right of review of the decision by the Mental Health Act Commission.

By Section 121(7) and (8) of the Act and the regulations, the Commission is given complete discretion in the way is should conduct this review (which must be made to it within six months of the receipt of the notice) and it may direct that the packet be not with-held.

B) Procedures for the exercise of the Commission's powers:

1) Relevant Special Hospital Panel (SHP) Executive Office or visiting Commissioner receive "appeal" from patient and/or sender of package. This need not necessarily be in writing.

2) A minimum of two, and not more than three Commissioners nominated by SHP convenor to review the decision.

3) Relevant Executive Officer notifies hospital of receipt of "appeal" and of the arrangements made by Commissioners to hear it, and asks for their written explanation of the grounds for withholding the package or item within the terms of Section 134(1) and (2) and the details of the procedure they have followed.

4) A visit should be arranged at which the following action should be taken.

   (a) If patient is appellant, Commissioners interview as on complaints visit.

   (b) If sender is appellant, Commissioners decide whether to invite him to be present or if written submission will suffice.

   (c) Commissioners should examine hospital's procedural documents to satisfy themselves that the requirements of the Act have been followed.

   (d) Commissioners to examine documents, article etc., with-held.

   (e) Commissioners, at their discretion, to interview all staff who had any direct influence on the particular decision to with-hold.

   (f) Commissioners to interview the person appointed by the managers, who has with-held the package or item, especially if considering over-riding the decision.

(N.B: If appropriate and parties agree Commissioners could interview appellant and parties (e) and (f) together).

5) Commissioners make decision and notify appellant(s) and managers in writing. If the Commissioners think it is desirable, and especially if the patient is mentally impaired, they may also tell the patient orally.

6) Commissioners consider whether cases raise any issues which should be reported to SHP team meeting, relevant National Standing Committee meeting or Central Policy Committee.

APPENDIX 15

POLICY ON RACE

Introduction

The Race Relations Act 1976 defines two kinds of racial discrimination:

Direct discrimination arises where a person treats another person less favourably on racial grounds than he treats, or would treat, someone else. "Racial grounds" means any of the following grounds: colour, race, nationality (including citizenship) or ethnic or national origins.

Indirect discrimination consists of treatment which may be described as equal in a formal sense as between different racial groups but discriminatory in its effect on one particular group. A 'racial group' is one defined by reference to one or more of the following: colour, race, nationality (including citizenship) or ethnic or national origins.

In upholding Race Relations legislation applicable to the whole of Great Britain, the Mental Health Act Commission is committed to the following aims and actions.

Aims

1.1 To ensure equality of opportunity to all members and staff of the Commission to participate in the organisation and work of the Commission irrespective of race, colour, culture or nationality.

1.2 To ensure that detained patients and others dealt with by the Commission are treated equally, irrespective of race etc. (as above).

1.3 To ensure that Health Authorities, Social Services Departments and other agencies concerned with the treatment/care of detained patients deliver such treatment/care equally, irrespective of race etc. (as above).

Actions

2.1 Confronting Racism

2.1 The Commission will take positive action to:

Prevent and counteract the effects of discriminatory practice on racial grounds by any member of the Commission, its staff or anyone acting on behalf of the Commission.

To ensure that issues concerning racial and cultural matters will not be 'marginalised'; such 'marginalisation' will be construed as 'indirect discrimination' and treated as such under this policy.

2.2 Training

For those who have not already undertaken similar training, the Commission will provide training for its members and staff in:

The personal awareness of racism, the recognition of racist practices and behaviour, and the ways in which racism may be counteracted within the Commission.

The recognition and ways of counteracting racism within Health Authorities, Departments of Social Services and other agencies concerned with the treatment/care of detained patients.

2.3 Work of Commission

2.3.1 The Commission will ensure that its policies, procedures and activities are free of discriminatory practices on racial grounds.

2.3.2 The Commission will endeavour to ensure that policies, procedures and activities of Health Authorities and Social Service Departments are free of discriminatory practices on racial grounds.

2.4 **Members of the Commission**

The Commission will ensure that all its members are involved in the work of the Commission according to their knowledge and experience, taking note of any special knowledge they may have through personal experience of racial and cultural issues; no member will be excluded from any of the Commission's activities on the grounds of race.

2.5 **Advice on Race Relations and Monitoring**

The Commission will instruct its Standing Committee on Race and Culture to:

1. To study and report on issues of race and culture as they relate to the Commission's work.

2. To advise the CPC and the Commission on relevant issues and to contribute to the promotion of a greater understanding within the Commission of matters relevant to race and culture and the development of Commission policies, procedures and practice that reflects that understanding.

3. To monitor the implementation of any policy promulgated by and for the Commission and to make proposals for updating where necessary.

4. To prepare material for the Biennial Report.

5. To undertake other relevant tasks as referred to by the Commission, CPC or the Chief Executive.

Publications used for reference

Home Office and the Central Office of Information (1977) *Racial Discrimination. A Guide to the Race Relations Act 1976*, HMSO, London.

Kalsi, Nirveen and Constantinides, Pamela (1989) *Working towards Racial Equality in Health Care. The Haringey Experience*, Kings Fund Centre, London.

King's Fund Equal Opportunities Task Force (1989) *Health Authority Equal Opportunities Committees*, King's Fund Publishing Office, London.

Mind Policy Paper 2 (1986) *Mental Health Services in a Multi-Racial Society*, MIND *Publications*, London.

Background reading

Britain, A and Maynard, M (1984) *Sexism, Racism and Oppression*, Blackwell, Oxford.

Fornando, Suman (1989) *Race and Culture in Psychiatry*, Tavistock/Routledge, London.

Husband, Charles (ed.) (1982) *'Race' in Britain,* Hutchinson, London.

Kovel, Joel (1988) *White Racism. A Psychohistory*, Free Association Books, London.

Sartre, Jean-Paul (1948) A*nti-Semite and Jew*, Translated by GJ Becker, Schocken Books, New York.

Approved by the Central Policy Committee on 1 February 1990

APPENDIX 16

MENTAL HEALTH ACT COMMISSION

MEMORANDUM
to the
Secretary of State for Health
on the
MENTAL HEALTH ACT 1983

SUBMITTED 30TH SEPTEMBER 1993

Memorandum to the Secretary of State for Health on the Mental Health Act 1993, submitted by the Mental Health Act Commission 30th September 1993

In its report of the internal review of the **Legal Powers on the Care of Mentally Ill People in the Community (August 1993)** the Department of Health noted that the Mental Health Act Commission considers *"that a full review of the 1983 Act is now needed"* (Annex F. page 62). The Department's brief from the Secretary of State had been to consider urgently, in the light of a proposal from the Royal College of Psychiatrists for introducing into the law a Community Supervision Order, how effective the existing legal powers are to ensure that mentally disordered people in the community get the care they need. The report stated that it was not possible to look at the issue of legal powers *"without taking account of the wider context in which the great majority of mentally ill people are now looked after in the community"* (paragraph 4, page 3). The Commission, in pointing out various legal powers for proposals or suggested legislative change or amendment, has likewise considered such powers in the wider context of the mental health system. It is the system, both in its legal framework and practice in delivering services to patients which needs reviewing. Does the 1983 Act match today's needs of all those with mental disorder in England and Wales, or is it, as described recently by the House of Commons Health Committee, "obsolescent, though far from obsolete" (Health Committee, 1993, paragraph 87)?.

Before listing and commenting on the specific statutory provisions which seem ripe for review and reform, the Commission makes a general observation about post war mental health legislation, both in its historical context and in its contemporary social setting, as it relates to existing facilities and services.

The predecessor to the Mental Health Act 1983 — the Mental Health Act 1959 — was based on the Report of the Royal Commission on Law relating to Mental Illness and Mental Deficiency (The Percy Report). It established the modern mental health legislation, repealing all existing legislation for mental illness and mental deficiency. One of its basic premises was that people suffering from mental disorder should, as far as possible, be treated no differently from the way in which society treats those suffering from physical illness. Hence compulsion and custody should be resorted to sparingly, employing the principle of the least restrictive alternative. Treatability of the patient in conditions of detention was the hallmark of a civilised mental health law. The emphasis on informal admission reflected in the 1959 Act was, therefore, institutionally orientated. For the minority of patients for whom compulsory powers were needed, decisions on admissions were to be a medical matter, and not judicial. A range of safeguards was enacted for those who had to be compulsorily detained. Only the provisions for Guardianship focused on treatment in the community, but, at that time psychiatric services were rapidly developing out-patient and domiciliary treatment, as well as facilities for in-patient care in some general hospital settings.

In January 1975 the Government announced its intention to review the 1959 Act. It did so in the wake of changes in psychiatric services and in public attitudes about mental health, and in the light of a number of important European Court of Human Right cases, principally "X v United Kingdom". A major factor in inducing the review was the report of the Committee on Mentally Abnormal Offenders (The Butler Committee). An interdepartmental committee of officials then started off the protracted process that led to the legislation in 1982. The general philosophy behind the proposals was the need to strengthen the rights and interests of detained patients, clarifying the balance between the safeguarding of patients' rights, interests and liberties with the safety of the public and hospital staff. Notwithstanding the introduction of community psychiatric nursing services and alternatives to admission to hospital such as crisis intervention schemes, the 1983 Act continued to have as its primary focus institutional care. The Mental Health Act Commission was brought into existence as an important element in the protection of the rights and interest of patients; in practice almost exclusively for detained patients. There was thus no replica of the Scottish Mental Welfare Commission which, in 1960, had been established to oversee the whole of the mental health system north of the border.

Two things about the time-tabling of law reform in the late 70s and early 80's should be noted. First, the period of legislative action — a quarter of a century — reflected the changed attitudes and practices which had taken place in treatment and care of patients, in the pattern of psychiatric services for the mentally disordered, and in public attitudes generally. Similarly in the last 10 years, practices (embodied in the Code of Practice since 1989) no less significant than in the previous 25 years have advanced; people have developed; psychiatric services for mentally disordered have changed, and are continuing to change as can be seen in the reports of the Reed Committee; the care and treatment of those with learning difficulties are being progressively de-institutionalised; and the shift from hospital based treatment to community care has significantly altered public attitudes and prompted new practices among mental health professionals. For many of those with acute mental disorder the nature of the care provided to them has changed from long stay hospitalisation to short stay, with frequent re-admissions.

The period of gestation of 7 years up to the Mental Health (Amendment) Act 1982 (substantially codified in the 1983 Act although certain provisions in the 1959 Act were not repealed) indicates many topics of controversy, as well as areas of consensus, all of which require extensive consultation with a wide range of organisations and individuals. The consultative process which would follow the publication of the report of the full review of the 1983 Act would entail legislative action not much sooner than the end of the century. Appropriately, a well designed mental health law could be in place for the 21st century.

The other matter to be noted is the philosophical basis of both the 1959 and 1983 Acts. Both Acts primarily focused on the powers of compulsory admission to hospital and mental nursing homes (it is worth observing that many of the units which now accommodate detained patients are smaller and more "residential" type establishments, unlike the conception of a large institution envisaged by Parliament in 1983). Part II of the 1983 Act, apart from Sections 7 to 10, deals with compulsory admission to hospital and the consequential provisions. Part III of the Act is concerned exclusively with patients hospitalised by order of a criminal court, including the power to transfer patients from prison to hospital. Part IV of the Act dealing with consent to treatment is largely directed to the imposition of medication and to other invasive treatment on detained patients in hospitals and mental nursing homes. Part V, in the role and function of the Mental Health Review Tribunals, relate exclusively to the discharge of the patients detained in hospital and mental nursing homes. Part VI deals primarily with the removal and return of detained patients within the UK.

It is only when the statute comes to Part VII — dealing with the management of property and the affairs of patients through the Court of Protection — that mentally disordered persons generally are catered for, irrespective of their care and treatment within or without hospital or mental nursing homes. Part VIII brings into play the social services, but primarily establishes the form of approval of social workers involved in the process of compulsory admission of mentally disordered people. Section 117 imposes a duty on social services and health authorities to provide aftercare services for most patients ceasing to be detained in hospital. The practical significance of this section has grown immeasurably in recent years, although it is interesting to note that it was an after-thought in the legislative process since the Government, at the time, argued that the inclusion of this section in the 1982 Amendment Act was superfluous because of the statutory duty already existing for health authorities and local authorities to provide aftercare facilities for mentally disordered patients discharged from hospital.

It is at the very least arguable that the radical transformation of mental health services, from being primarily hospital-based to community-focused, should be reflected in the legislative framework. In short, the legislation should give priority to provisions for care and treatment in the community — the proposed "supervised discharge order" is an example of a new form of compulsory care in the community. Compulsory admission powers, while extremely important in terms of loss of liberty, should reflect society's resort to hospitalisation sparingly and secondarily. At the same time a review might provide an opportunity to frame legislation which, whilst recognising the importance of patient rights and professional discretion does not merely find a new location on that particular pendulum, but also takes into account the new, radically different, approaches to mental health law that have developed in recent years. In particular, the development of concepts of therapeutic jurisprudence (see for example: Therapeutic jurisprudence: Developments in Mental Health Law.

Carson D and Wexler D B (in press)) with its emphasis on an essentially inter-disciplinary and co-operative approach and its concern to see that services are effective in the community as well as in institution provides an important new dimension to the theoretical framework which at the very least is worth considering.

There are, apart from the presentational structure of the 1983 Act, five main reasons why the Commission invites the Secretary of State to start the process for developing new legislation in the field of mental health, by a thorough review of the law and practice.

1. *The institutional services on which both the 1959 and 1983 Acts were premised are rapidly disappearing. There are fewer large hospitals delivering acute care for short periods. The focus is distinctly on care in the community. This development is presenting practical problems. The Commission has been receiving an increasing number of queries about the definition of a hospital. Section 145(1) of the 1983 Act defines a hospital as an NHS establishment and "any accommodation provided by a local authority and used as a hospital or on behalf of the Secretary of State" under NHS legislation. Mentally ill people are being detained in health authority owned hostels which fall within the definition. But if this is legally correct, does it reflect a policy of good practice? Many suggest that there is a powerful argument in favour of compulsory admission to a mental health service, rather than committal to a defined place, such as a hospital or even a hostel.*

    Another aspect of the current mental health scene is the care and treatment of mentally disordered offenders accommodated in the penal system. Since prison hospitals are outside the terms of the 1983 Act, none of the Act's safeguards is available to mentally disordered prisoners. The relationship between the penal system and mental health services is a topic of much current concern.

ii. *The underlying objective of the 1959 Act was the delivery of psychiatric treatment for mental disorder with the minimum of legal impediment. While a modest dose of legalism was injected into the 1983 Act, which had not been in the 1959 Act, in order to clarify the balance between psychiatric treatment and individual freedom of choice, it is now recognised that mental health care is not just a potential conflict between psychiatrists and patients. Other professional groups, paramedical and non-medical are involved in patient care and treatment. There has emerged in recent years a much clearer articulation of the ethical principles governing the treatment of patients — principles which have evolved from multi-disciplinary groups. For example, it is widely stated now that if a person is detained for care and treatment, he or she is entitled to reasonable standard of care and treatment. Legislation does not directly address this issue.*

iii. *There are classes of people whose problems the Mental Health Act simply does not address. Mentally disordered children and young persons who are dealt with under the Children Act 1989 are not within the purview of mental health legislation. The interrelationship of child welfare and mental*

102

health needs attention. Mentally incapacitated people are not specifically catered for in the 1983 Act, although their needs have been impressively reviewed by the Law Commission.

iv. There are some immediate problems associated with the existing legislation, some of which were identified by the Mental Health Act Commission in its Fourth Biennial Report. (for convenience we annex paragraph 11.3, pages 44 and 45 of that report). We note additionally that the Reed Committee has suggested one or two amendments (principally, Section 48 of the 1983 Act). The Department itself has a list of deficiencies, the most notable of which relates to the discharge functions of managers and NHS trusts. (see v.d below).

v. The implementation of the NHS and Community Care Act 1990 has revolutionised the management and administrative context within which mental health services are provided.

a. The purchaser/provider divide has caused concerns over the responsibility for the actual provision, as well as the quality of provision of services. There is a need to clarify and possibly strengthen Section 140.

b. The purchase and provision of services which rely upon extra-contractual referrals (ECRs) are patchy and do not always meet the needs of the patients.

c. The Commission has come across examples where the preferred treatment which would be based on an ECR has been refused by the responsible health authority in favour of locally-provided care not necessarily, according to clinicians, in the best long term interests of the patient.

d. The non-executive directors of the NHS Trusts are the managers for the purpose of the Mental Health Act, but there are problems caused by the inability to co-opt others to this role in the hearing of appeals against detention and the renewal of detention. There is a greater concern about the role of the managers under Sections 20 and 23. There is a possible conflict of loyalties in managers protecting the interests of the patient and at the same time managing the Trust's resources to ensure maximum occupancy levels.

e. There needs to be a review of the situation where a fee paying patient in a private mental nursing home, registered to take detained patients, can be detained against his or her will and yet be compelled to pay the fees for this involuntary detention. Should such a patient be given a statutory right of detention, or transfer to an NHS hospital?

f. The rights of mentally disordered persons in group fund-holding practices needs to be clarified to ensure they receive the services they require at the right time. Evidence is emerging that some fund-holding practices are showing a reluctance to purchase the full range of community mental health services required.

g. The assessment provisions under Section 47 of the 1990 Act may need to be supplemented with directions in relation to the assessment of the mentally disordered and also in relation to the provision of services to prevent the patient from leaving. These powers are not clearly defined.

h. The physical treatment of the detained mentally disordered patient who refuses to give consent is outside Part IV of the Act, and is probably not covered by the decision in Re F. The proposals of the Law Commission Consultation Paper 129 may not provide the answer.

i. The House of Commons Health Committee (1992-93) Fifth Report recommended many areas for research, examination and evaluation prior to legislative changes. This work should proceed as soon as possible to ensure that the results can be taken on board by the reviewing body.

Since the publication of the Fourth Biennial Report the Commission has given further thought to a number of general issues relating to the 1983 Act. They are as follows:-

1. Who is a mentally disordered patient?

For some time there has been a debate over the inclusion of psychopathic disorder in the definition in Section 1(2) of the Act. We await with interest the deliberations of the Reed Working Party. Whatever conclusion is arrived at about the future of the psychopath, there will be a need to address the consequences of the recent decision of the High Court on 28th July 1993 in **R v Cannons Park Mental Health Review Tribunal, ex parte A**. The Court held that an untreatable psychopath, however much he or she is a danger to others (or to himself/herself) cannot lawfully be detained under the Mental Health Act 1983. But if a psychopath is no longer to be regarded as falling within mental health legislation, Section 1(2) will need to be amended so as to delete "psychopathic disorder" involving some consequential amendments. If the amendment is not made, active consideration will have to be given to the requirement of treatability in a case of compulsory admission. If the psychopath remains within mental health legislation, there may be a need to amend Section 3(2)(b) which qualifies compulsory admission for treatment, to treatment "likely to alleviate or prevent a deterioration" of the psychopath's condition.

2. Admission powers: Sections 2 and 3

Chapter 5 of the Mental Health Act Code of Practice provides some pointers as to when Section 2 or Section 3 should be used. The need to provide such advice is perhaps an indicator that the three Civil Admission sections (2, 3 and 4) are in need of review, principally in relation to how they relate to each other. Despite the advice in the Code it is clear to the Mental Health Act Commission that Section 2, given the clarification of the 1983 Act that patients detained under it can be treated in the absence of their consent under the provisions of Part IV, is being used in many cases as a short term treatment order, and not primarily as an assessment order. The safeguards offered by the Act in relation to Sections 2 and 3 are different.

Mental health legislation in Scotland and Northern Ireland offers different configurations of civil admission powers and the Commission would argue that the experience of Scotland and Northern Ireland as well as international provision will contribute to any review of admission arrangements in England and Wales.

3. Guardianship

The Department of Health in its recent internal review was keen to see Guardianship applied to a "wider range of patients", although not applicable to the group of patients whose health care needs are of crucial importance. Clearly, the role of Guardianship in the context of growing community care should be reviewed. Indeed in legislation that reflects the primacy of community care, guardianship would have a prominent position.

4. Leave of absence under Section 17

The Department of Health in its report of the internal review has recommended an amendment to Section 17 removing the 6 month time limit for leave of absence. In so recommending the Department is suggesting that the amendment should be considered only as an interim measure. Any longer period of time would involve at least an amendment to Section 20 because the prerequisite to the grant of leave is the liability of the patient being detained. The question of the grant of leave of absence at the sole instance of the Responsible Medical Officer (RMO) was raised in an acute form in the Commission's adjudication in 1991 on the gate pass system at Broadmoor. Is it right that such a power should be exercised without direct involvement of any other professionals on the staff of the hospital? If it were thought right to confirm the power to grant leave of absence other than on the RMO alone, the exclusivity of decision-making by the RMO in relation to the patient's care and treatment would have to be generally addressed.

5. Mentally Disordered Offenders

There are various aspects of Part III of the Act which call for attention:

i. Remands to hospital by the criminal courts under Section 35 and 36 have been the subject of criticism. First, it has been hotly debated whether a person detained in hospital under Section 35 for assessment and report to court can lawfully be treated without the patient's consent. (See paragraph 17.3 Code of Practice). The restriction on magistrates' courts to detain a person for psychi-

atric assessment only would need to be reviewed.

ii. **Restriction orders under Section 41**

The practice of the courts invariably to make a restriction order unlimited in time is questionable. There is also doubt whether the division of responsibility for discharge of restricted patients, between the Department of Health and the Home Office subject to the release powers of the Mental Health Review Tribunal is a satisfactory system of release mechanism.

iii. **Transfer to Hospital of prisoners**

Sections 47 to 50 will need review in the light of the report of the Reed Working Party and the development of psychiatric services in the prison system. No doubt the National Advisory Committee on Mentally Disordered Offenders will be examining the statutory provisions in both Parts III and VI of the Act.

Annexed is a detailed list of matters in relation to Court assessment procedures and mentally disordered persons which the Commission considers require review.

6. Consent to Treatment

The thorny topic of the absence of a patient's consent to a range of invasive treatment has been highlighted by the House of Lords decisions in **Re F (Mental Patients: Sterilisation) [1990] 2AC1** and **Airedale NHS Trust v Bland [1993] 2WLR316** in the allied field of mental incapacity. The Commission takes the view that Part IV of the Act needs to be reviewed in the light of the **UN Principles for the Protection of Persons with Mental Illness and the Improvement of Mental Health Care** (adopted by the General Assembly, 17th December 1991). The UN Principles recommend that a proposed plan of treatment may be given to a patient without informed consent, only if all of the following conditions are satisfied:

a. the patient is an involuntary patient;

b. an independent authority is satisfied the patient lacks the capacity to give or withhold informed consent to the proposed plan of treatment or, if domestic legislation so provides, that, having regard to the patient's own safety or the safety of others, the patient unreasonably withholds such consent; and

c. the independent authority is satisfied that the proposed plan of treatment is in the best interest of the patient's health.

Two specific issues arise in relation to the 1983 Act. First, is the SOAD system sufficiently "an independent authority"? Since the Mental Health Act Commission performs only the function of appointing a registered medical practitioner (and other non-medical persons in Section 57 cases only) for the purpose of providing a second opinion (and in Section 57 cases of verifying informed consent) the single registered medical practitioner probably does not qualify as "the independent authority". If the Mental Health Act Commission were to become the independent authority supplying a multi-disciplinary surveillance over detained patients treatment and their consent to it, contrary to the decision of **Morland J in R v Mental Health Act Commission, ex parte Witham (No 2)** this would represent a considerable extension of the Commission's work.

Second, the UN Principles do not cover treatment of detained patients by way of psychosurgery and other intrusive and irreversible treatment for mental illness. Such treatments it is recommended, should be carried out only where the patient has given informed consent and an independent body is satisfied that there is generally informed consent and that the treatment best serves the health needs of the patient. Subject to the restriction, that only the registered medical practitioner has to certify that the treatment should be given, having regard to the likelihood that the treatment will alleviate or prevent deterioration of the patient's condition, Section 57 of the 1983 Act would appear to conform to the UN Principles. Nevertheless the ethical propriety of psychosurgery deserves to be examined in the light of the experience since 1983.

The **Witham** (No: 1) case raised concerns about the correct interpretation of the capacity and consent provisions in Sections 57 and 58. The provisions require clarification in the light of the judgment of Lord Justice Stuart Smith (see Fourth Biennial Report, paragraphs 6.12 and 11.1, pages 32 and 43 respectively)

Ten years experience of the operation of Part IV (Consent to Treatment) of the Mental Health Act has raised a number of issues that require consideration, amongst which are;

i.   the present Part IV of the Act at Section 58 provides for the application of the same criteria in relation to the decision to administer treatment to a detained patient who is incapable of giving consent, as to one who is capable but unwilling. In general terms the Law Commission's recent consultation documents on Decision Making and Incapacitated Adults (it is recognised that the Commission specifically excluded consideration of Part IV of the Mental Health Act) are relevant in the former circumstances.

     The Commission would argue that, in relation to the latter circumstances, active consideration should be given to whether the legislation needs to make clearer provision as to the grounds upon which a refusing competent detained patient can be compelled to accept treatment.

ii. The Commission feels strongly that the present "three months" rule (Section 58(1)(b)) applied to the administration of medication needs to be reviewed. At the time of the passage of the Mental Health Act (Amendment) Bill 1982 the Parliamentary Under Secretary of State said "the three months gives time for the psychiatrist to consider a treatment programme which suits the patient. Three months seems to fit in best with both clinical experience and clinical practice. It is long enough to allow a proper valuation and assessment of what, if any, long term treatment may be needed. It is also short enough to ensure that patients' consent, or a second opinion, is obtained before a long term course of drug treatment gets too far ahead" (Special Standing Committee, June 29 1982).

     With ten years further experience of the administration of medication for mentally disordered people and, in view of the rising concern about the safety of certain medications for mental disorder, it would seem, at the very least, that this particular aspect of the provisions of Part IV of the Mental Health Act needs to be examined. At the same time, the desirability of making the Act's various holding powers (eg: Sections 5, 135 and 136) susceptible to statutory consent to treatment safeguards should be considered.

iii. Commissioners have been concerned for some time that, within the framework of Part IV, the key task of assessing the capacity of the patient to consent to treatment, which rests with the patient's RMO, together with the need for subsequent regular reviews of such capacity has not been undertaken with the thoroughness it deserves. Active consideration needs to be given to strengthening the Act's provisions in this regard.

7. **Mental Health Review Tribunals**

Although the Mental Health Act Commission has no power to discharge an inappropriately detained patient — a power which is a preserve of managers and of the Mental Health Review Tribunals — it does have the duty to keep under review the powers and duties respectively conferred or imposed by the Act.

The Commission notes that there is now a considerable body of jurisprudence on the provisions of Part V of the Act which have pointed up difficulties, such as the construction of Section 72(1): **see Mr Justice Sedley in R v Cannons Park Mental Health Review Tribunal ex parte A, 28th July 1993, page 17DFF noted above.** In the case of discharge of an unrestricted patient, the burden of proof is on the patient to satisfy the tribunal of any one of the criteria. These criteria are framed in negative form. The hospital does not have to prove that the grounds exist; it is up to the patient to prove that they do not: see Hoggett Mental Health law (1990) page 283. It seems that the tribunals in practice apply a criminal standard of proof rather than be satisfied on the balance of probabilities: see Peay, Tribunals on Trial (1989) page 211.

The power to discharge restricted patients under Section 73 also give rise to the burden of proof - in that case the patient has to satisfy the tribunal of a double negative. The *admissibility before the European Commission of Human Rights recently of the Kaye Case, and the hint that the Commission looks with disfavour upon the heavy burden on a patient to gain his or her discharge, suggests that these two sections, indeed the whole of Part V, will demand instant review as and when the Kaye decision emerges from Strasbourg. Indeed, it is arguable that this case could have as powerful an impact on future mental health legislation in England and Wales as did "X v United Kingdom" (see page 2)*

8. Court of Protection

Part VII of the Act is excluded from review by the Commission: see Section 120 Subsection 7. Issues relating to the protection of the property rights and interests of patients have, therefore, not been the concern of the Commission. Nevertheless the Commission is aware of some dissatisfaction with the role and function and the Court of Protection, in that the management of the property and affairs of mentally disordered people cannot sensibly be detached from their care and treatment.

9. The Mental Health Act Commission

Commissioners will submit under separate cover proposals for changes in its role and function. The proposals do not envisage the need for primary legislation, but the role of a watchdog body in the field of mental health would be an important aspect of any review of the 1983 Act. The overlapping functions and responsibilities of the Health Advisory Service, Social Services Inspectorate and the Mental Health Act Commission are worthy of attention.

CONCLUSION

This memorandum has not provided an exhaustive list of proposed or suggested changes in the law relating to mental health. It seeks merely to highlight two things:

1. *The incremental distancing of mental health services from those which pertained in the 1970s, and for which Parliament was appropriately legislating in the early 1980s, is such as to call for legislation, to match the substantially changed environment of mental health services, in the facilities for care and treatment, psychiatric practices and public expectation of the services for the mentally disordered.*

2. *There is a growing clamour for such a review of the 1983 Act from the public: see the comments of various national newspapers on the Secretary of State's ten-point plan for developing successful and safe community care and her plan to introduce a Bill in Parliament to provide for supervised discharge of psychiatric patients.*

The review process should start now, appropriately coinciding with the Tenth Anniversary of the 1983 Act. The reason for a start now are three:

1. The gap between the reality of the service and legislation is widening. The 1983 Act will become increasingly irrelevant to the available services. For example, when the Commission began visiting hospitals in

1983, it identified some 523 hospitals and mental nursing homes for its visiting programme — a manageable task. Today there are 600 or more units accommodating detained patients which the Commission has a duty to visit as "hospitals" within, it thinks, the definition in Section 145.

2. The Law Commission will be completing its report on the law relating to incapacitated adults. Much of that report will need to be dovetailed into mental health law. It will be desirable that issues relating to mental health should be treated in one Mental Health Act, and not just what the 1983 is in effect — namely, a Mental Illness Detention Act.

3. Starting now, with the time scale not very different from that experienced in the 1982 legislation, would provide ample opportunity for extensive consultation and sensible debate over often delicate topics. It would avoid the delay that occurred in the producing of the Code of Practice due to the Commission's failure to consult during the framing of its recommended Code: see Cavadino M. Public Law (1993 Summer Issue). The review would proceed at a reasonably leisurely pace which would benefit all those in the mental health system as well as administrators, legislators and the public. It would not be helpful if in two or three years time there was suddenly an urge to review the Act and the reviewers were put under constraints of time to produce a report. The experience of the Royal Commission on Criminal Justice which had imposed on it a time limit of 2 years within which to report demonstrates that it is not a sensible way of proceeding to reform areas of social policy.

* The annexes referred to in the Memorandum are not included

30TH SEPTEMBER 1993

APPENDIX 17

PUBLICATIONS AVAILABLE FROM THE COMMISSION

1. Form MHAC 1 (Section 61 Review Form)

2. Commission Information Leaflet

3. MHAC Practice Note No: 1 —
   Guidance on the Administration of Clozapine and other treatments requiring blood tests under the provisions of Part IV of the Mental Health Act

Shortly to be published:—

1. A leaflet about the Commission and complaints for patients and carers

2. A leaflet about the Commission and consent to treatment safeguards for patients and carers

3. MHAC Practice Notes:—

   a. The administration of medication for mental disorder, the Mental Health Act and Nurses;

   b. Section 5(2) of the Mental Health Act, and Transfers;

If you are interested in receiving any of the above please fill the form over the page.

Other relevant publications

The revised edition of the Mental Health Act 1983 Code of Practice was published on the 27 August 1993. It is available from all HMSO stockists priced £4.50.
(ISBN 0 11 321624 6)

Mental Health Act Commission
Maid Marian House
56 Hounds Gate
Nottingham
NG2 6BG

Please send me

.... copies of Form MHAC 1

.... copies of the Commission Information Leaflet

.... Practice Note — Guidance on the Administration of Clozapine and other treatments requiring blood tests under the provisions of Part IV of the Mental Health Act.

I would like to be included on the Commission's circulation list to receive future Commission publications.

Please tick appropriate box.

YES	NO

NAME: . . . .

ADDRESS: . . . .

. . . .

. . . .

APPENDIX 18

EVALUATION OF 5TH BIENNIAL REPORT OF THE MENTAL HEALTH ACT COMMISSION

Dear Reader

We hope that you have found this report useful and informative. It would be helpful if you would complete and return this questionnaire to the address given below.

The Commission would like to make its Biennial Reports as "user friendly" as possible. We would appreciate your comments on this Report, and any suggestions for change in the future.

Thank you for your assistance.

Yours sincerely

SIR LOUIS BLOM-COOPER QC

	1. EXCELLENT	2. VERY GOOD	3. GOOD	4. AVERAGE	5. BELOW AVERAGE	6. POOR
CONTENT OF REPORT						
STYLE						
LAYOUT						
STATISTICAL INFORMATION						
PRESENTATION						
IF YOU HAVE COMPLETED BOXES 4-6 INDICATE HOW YOU THINK THE REPORT COULD HAVE BEEN IMPROVED						
ANY OTHER GENERAL COMMENTS AND/OR SUGGESTIONS FOR FUTURE REPORTS						

Mental Health Act Commission
Maid Marian House
56 Houds Gate
Nottingham NG1 6BG

INDEX

114

Printed in the United Kingdom for HMSO.
Dd.0297612, 12/93, C34, 3396/4, 5673, 267209.